Grilled chicken with cucumber and herb salad, page 67

About WW

Weight Watchers is a global wellness company and the world's leading commercial weight management program. We inspire millions of people to adopt healthy habits for real life. Through our engaging digital experience and face-to-face group meetings, members follow our livable and sustainable program that encompasses healthy eating, physical activity and positive mindset. With more than five decades of experience in building communities and our deep expertise in behavioral science, we aim to deliver wellness for all. To learn more about the Weight Watchers approach to healthy living, please visit www.weightwatchers.com. For more information about our global business, visit our corporate website at www.weightwatchersinternational.com.

Roast chicken with meyer lemons and shallot sauce, page 186

Contents

About our recipes, vi

Introduction: Let's eat more chicken!, viii

Poultry primer, x

    All about chicken, x

    All about turkey, xi

    Poultry labeling: meaningful or just marketing?, xii

    White meat vs. dark meat, xiii

    Five tips for safety and freshness, xiv

Chapter 1
Quick chicken dinners in 20 minutes or less, 1

Chapter 2
Dinner on the grill, 41

Chapter 3
Salads & sandwiches, 77

Chapter 4
One-pan dinners, 113

Chapter 5
Comforting classics, 147

Chapter 6
Sunday roasts, 179

Recipes by SmartPoints® value, 205

Index, 207

About our recipes

While losing weight isn't only about what you eat, Weight Watchers realizes the critical role it plays in your success and overall good health. That's why our philosophy is to offer great-tasting, easy recipes that are nutritious as well as delicious. Our recipes emphasize the kinds of healthy foods we love: lots of fresh fruits and vegetables, most of which have 0 SmartPoints value, and lean proteins, some of which have 0 SmartPoints and others that are low in SmartPoints. We also try to ensure that our recipes fall within the recommendations of the U.S. Dietary Guidelines for Americans—lower in saturated fat and sugar with plenty of fruits and vegetables, lean proteins, and low-fat dairy—so they support a diet that promotes health and reduces the risk for disease. If you have special dietary needs, consult with your health-care professional for advice on a diet that is best for you, then adapt these recipes to meet your specific nutritional needs.

Get started, keep going, and enjoy good nutrition

At Weight Watchers, we believe that eating well makes life better, no matter where you are in your weight-loss journey. These tasty recipes are ideal, whether you're just getting started or have already reached your goals on the SmartPoints system. Unlike other weight-loss programs, which focus solely on calories, the SmartPoints system guides you toward healthier foods that are lower in sugar and saturated fat, and higher in protein. But this isn't a diet—all food is "in." Eating well should be fun, energizing, and delicious, so that healthy food choices become second nature. To get maximum satisfaction, we suggest you keep the following information in mind while preparing our recipes:

- On the WW Freestyle™ program, eating a mix of foods (rather than all zero Points® meals) can help you avoid feeling bored or deprived. Remember, there's room for all SmartPoints foods in your plan—variety is key to a healthy and livable eating style.

- SmartPoints values are given for each recipe. The SmartPoints value for each ingredient is assigned based on the number of calories and the amount of saturated fat, sugar, and protein in each ingredient. The SmartPoints values for each ingredient are then added together and divided by the number of servings, and the result is rounded.

- Recipes include approximate nutritional information: They are analyzed for Calories (Cal), Total Fat, Saturated Fat (Sat Fat), Sodium (Sod), Total Carbohydrates (Total Carb), Sugar, Dietary Fiber (Fib), and Protein (Prot). The nutritional values are obtained from the Weight Watchers database, which is maintained by registered dietitians.

- To boost flavor, we often include fresh herbs or a squeeze of citrus instead of increasing the salt. If you don't need to restrict your sodium intake, feel free to add a touch more salt as desired.

- Recipes in this book that are designated gluten free do not contain any wheat (in all forms, including kamut, semolina, spelt, and triticale), barley, or rye, or any products that are made from these ingredients, such as breads, couscous, pastas, seitan, soy sauce, beer, malt vinegar, and malt beverages. Other foods such as salad dressings, Asian-style sauces, salsa and tomato sauce, shredded cheese, yogurt, and sour cream may be sources of gluten. Check ingredient labels carefully on packaged foods that we call for, as different brands of the same premade food product may or may not contain gluten. If you are following a gluten-free diet because you have celiac disease, please consult your health-care professional.

- Recipe introductory headnote suggestions and Freestyle it tips have a SmartPoints value of 0 unless otherwise stated.

- For information about the Weight Watchers plan, please visit WeightWatchers.com/us/m/cms/plan-basics.

Calculations not what you expected?

SmartPoints values for the recipes in this book are calculated without counting the zero Points foods—fruits, most vegetables, and some lean proteins that are part of the plan. However, the nutritional information does include the nutrient content of these ingredients. This means you may notice discrepancies with the SmartPoints value you calculate using the nutrition information provided for the recipe versus the SmartPoints value listed for the recipe. That's because the SmartPoints values for the recipes that contain zero Points ingredients have been adjusted to reflect those ingredients, while the nutrition information provided includes the nutrition for all of the ingredients. For tracking purposes, use the SmartPoints value listed for the recipe. Also, please note, when fruits and veggies are liquefied or pureed (as in a smoothie), their nutrient content is incorporated into the recipe calculations. These nutrients can increase the SmartPoints.

Alcohol is included in our SmartPoints calculations. Because alcohol information is generally not included on nutrition labels, it's not an option you can include when using the handheld or online SmartPoints calculator or the Weight Watchers app. But since we include the alcohol information that we get from our database in our recipes, you might notice discrepancies between the SmartPoints you see here in our recipes and the values you get using the calculator. The SmartPoints listed for our recipes are the most accurate values.

Simply Filling (the no-count option)

If counting SmartPoints isn't your thing, try Simply Filling, a no-count technique. To follow it, eat just until satisfied, primarily from the list of Simply Filling foods found in the Tracker online. For more information, see your meeting-room materials or go online if you are a subscriber.

Choosing ingredients

As you learn to eat more healthfully and add more wholesome foods to your meals, consider these:

Lean meats and poultry

Purchase lean meats and poultry, and trim them of all visible fat before cooking. When poultry is cooked with the skin on, we recommend removing the skin before eating. Nutritional information for recipes that include meat, poultry, and fish is based on cooked skinless, boneless portions (unless otherwise stated) with the fat trimmed.

Seafood

Whenever possible, our recipes call for seafood that is sustainable and deemed the most healthful for human consumption so that your choice of seafood is not only good for the oceans but also good for you. For more information about the best seafood choices and to download a pocket guide, go to the Environmental Defense Fund at seafood.edf.org, the Monterey Bay Aquarium at seafoodwatch.org, or the Safina Center at safinacenter.org.

Produce

For the best flavor, maximum nutrient content, and the lowest prices, buy fresh, local produce such as vegetables, leafy greens, and fruits in season. Rinse them thoroughly before using, and keep a supply of cut-up vegetables and fruits in your refrigerator for convenient healthy snacks.

Whole grains

Explore your market for whole-grain products such as whole wheat and whole-grain breads and pastas, brown rice, bulgur, barley, cornmeal, whole wheat couscous, oats, farro, and quinoa to enjoy with your meals.

Let's eat more chicken!

We think it's a whole new world when it comes to poultry, and that's why we're so excited about bringing you *The All New Chicken Cookbook*. Our members never stop asking for more delicious ways to prepare it, and we think there's never been a better time to enjoy it. Not only are there more choices than ever when it comes to poultry—from how it's raised, farm to table, to an ever-widening variety of cuts and products—but skinless chicken and turkey breast are now zero Points foods. That means you can enjoy these fabulous foods every day and never have to track them. And skinless dark meat cuts (think thighs and drumsticks) are low enough in SmartPoints that you'll want to savor them as well.

Chicken is nutritious, delicious, and versatile, a partner to flavors both bold and comforting. It's perfect for the kind of weeknight meals many of us aspire to prepare even on the busiest days. It's also famous as the centerpiece for luscious Sunday dinners. And don't forget turkey: A host of new cuts and products available year-round have taken it well beyond the Thanksgiving table.

The 130 inspired Weight Watchers kitchen-tested recipes in this book will expand your poultry horizons and guarantee you never have to settle for less-than-scrumptious meals again. Even in just a few minutes you can put together a tempting home-cooked meal that's high in protein, big on flavor, and perfect for weight loss.

We've also included information throughout the book that we know our readers want. Our Poultry primer can answer just about any question you've ever had about chicken and turkey, from what a broiler-fryer is to what terms like "free-range" and "air-chilled" mean when it comes to taste and quality. And in every chapter you'll find how-tos on subjects like making aromatic rubs and marinades, easily carving whole birds, and selecting the best store-bought rotisserie chicken. Because the more you know, the better will be your health and happiness.

We hope you enjoy it all—one meal after another.

Chicken bahn mi sandwiches, page 101

Poultry primer

"A chicken in every pot!" It's a hopeful slogan from the depression era, one we think is just as relevant today. This section is full of information to help you navigate an ever-expanding world of choices. We start with the common terms you'll see on poultry labels—what they mean and their relationship to quality (and often price)— then delve into the essential makeup and nutrition of different types and cuts of chicken and turkey, plus tips for storing poultry for freshness and safety.

All about chicken

Ever wondered about the difference between a broiler and a roaster, or what a Cornish game hen really is? Here are the various types of chicken and close relatives that are commonly available in supermarkets, butcher shops, and farmers' markets, as well as online, followed by a rundown of standard chicken pieces and their nutritional value.

Broiler-fryer

Broiler-fryers are the most commonly available birds in supermarkets and also the most versatile. Although defined as weighing in at 2½ to 4½ pounds, it's difficult to find one weighing less than 3 pounds in today's market. Their size means they roast in about an hour, or they can be broken down into eight pieces or into quarters for a wide assortment of cooking methods. A whole broiler-fryer will serve four to six people.

Roaster

Weighing between 5 and 7 pounds, these hefty chickens are older than broiler chickens and good for feeding a crowd. As their name suggests, they're most often roasted whole and can feed up to eight thanks to a good quantity of breast meat. A big 7-pound roaster can take up to two hours to cook, so some advance planning is necessary.

Capon

A castrated rooster weighing from 8 to 10 pounds, the capon is a French specialty that is usually available only through butchers. Plump and juicy, it's a great choice for holiday dinners and can be roasted (and even brined) any way you would prepare a small turkey.

Cornish game hen

Weighing in at 1 to 2 pounds, these petite birds are a cross between Cornish Game and White Plymouth Rock chickens. Although it's called a hen, it can be either male or female. Their small size means they cook up quickly, making them particularly convenient; they can be roasted or baked in the oven, stuffed or unstuffed, or they can be spatch-cocked (split open to lie flat) or quartered for easy grilling. A smaller hen will feed one, while a larger hen is perfect for sharing between two diners.

Chicken by the numbers

Here's a rundown of favorite chicken pieces. All nutritional information is for raw skinless portions.

Breast (boneless)

Best for: Breading, grilling, poaching, sautéing, soup, steaming, stir-frying
Nutrition (5 ounces): 168 Cal, 32 g Prot, 4 g Total Fat, 1 g Sat Fat. 0 SmartPoints value

Bone-in breast

Best for: Baking, grilling, poaching, roasting, sheet-pan dinners, soup
Nutrition (7 ounces): 239 Cal, 45 g Prot, 5 g Total Fat, 1 g Sat Fat. 0 SmartPoints value

Ground breast

Best for: Baking, burgers, sautéing, soup, stew
Nutrition (4 ounces): 141 Cal, 25 g Prot, 2 g Total Fat, 0 g Sat Fat. 0 SmartPoints value

Drumstick (bone-in)

Best for: Baking, braising, grilling, oven-frying, roasting, sheet-pan dinners
Nutrition (1 drumstick; about 4½ ounces): 144 Cal, 26 g Prot, 4 g Total Fat, 1 g Sat Fat. 2 SmartPoints value

Thigh (boneless)

Best for: Baking, braising, grilling, roasting, sautéing, sheet-pan dinners, soup, stew, stir-frying
Nutrition (5 ounces): 171 Cal, 28 g Prot, 6 g Total Fat, 2 g Sat Fat. 3 SmartPoints value

Wing (bone-in)

Best for: Baking, roasting, stock
Nutrition (1 wing; about 2 ounces): 71 Cal, 12 g Prot, 2 g Total Fat, 1 g Sat Fat. 1 SmartPoints value

All about turkey

The majority of turkeys sold in the United States are White Holland breed. Most are 4 to 8 months old, ranging from 8 to 24 pounds. Here are a few special terms to keep in mind when selecting whole turkeys, and then a roundup of turkey cuts that are typically available outside whole-turkeys' autumn season.

Fresh

Rather than being flash-frozen and stored for weeks or months, "fresh" turkeys are chilled to 26°F and sold quickly to ensure quality. If properly handled, differences in flavor and texture between fresh and frozen turkeys are minimal, so keep that in mind before paying a premium for a fresh turkey. If you do opt for fresh, remember to cook it within 2 days of purchase.

Heirloom and heritage

These birds belong to diverse breeds that were nearly completely phased out over the last 50 years, as turkeys were bred almost exclusively for mass production. Some names you may see are Bourbon Red, Narragansett, Standard Bronze, and more, plus any number of cross-bred heritage species. These turkeys grow more slowly, require room to roam, and typically have less white meat than commercial species. Not surprisingly, you'll pay substantially more for these birds and may have to special-order them from a butcher or supplier. The upside? Connoisseurs claim their meat boasts superior flavor, and you can feel good about helping to preserve agricultural diversity and supporting small-scale farming.

Hen or tom

Although there are minor differences in the bone structures of males (toms) and females (hens), most experts agree that factors such as age and diet, not gender, are important in determining tenderness and flavor.

Self-basting

These turkeys have been injected with a mixture of liquid, fats, salt, and sometimes chemicals intended to keep the meat moist during cooking; read the label carefully to make sure there are no ingredients you object to. Does self-basting produce a moist turkey? It may, but brining your turkey yourself, or plumping it with your choice of liquids via an injector (it looks like a large hypodermic needle) gives you more control over the ingredients used and will save you from paying for extra water weight (usually between 5% and 9%) when you purchase your turkey.

Turkey by the numbers

Whole turkey is the hands-down bestseller every November, but there are a number of other options that are usually available year-round. All nutritional information is for raw skinless portions unless otherwise indicated.

Bone-in breast (4 to 8 pounds)

Best for: Baking, roasting
Nutrition (3 ounces boneless cooked): 125 Cal, 26 g Prot, 2 g Total Fat, 1 g Sat Fat. 0 SmartPoints value

Boneless breast (3 to 5 pounds)

Best for: Baking, grilling, roasting
Nutrition (3 ounces cooked): 125 Cal, 26 g Prot, 2 g Total Fat, 1 g Sat Fat. 0 SmartPoints value

Ground skinless breast

Best for: Burgers, soups, casseroles, tacos
Nutrition (4 ounces): 126 Cal, 27 g Prot, 2 g Total Fat, 0 g Sat Fat. 0 SmartPoints value

Ground turkey (regular white & dark meat)

Best for: Burgers, soups, casseroles, tacos
Nutrition (4 ounces): 167 Cal, 22 g Prot, 9 g Total Fat, 2 g Sat Fat. 4 SmartPoints value

Breast cutlets

Best for: Grilling, sautéing, sheet-pan dinners, soup, stir-frying
Nutrition (5 ounces): 143 Cal, 30 g Prot, 2 g Total Fat, 1 g Sat Fat. 0 SmartPoints value

Drumstick

Best for: Baking, grilling, braising, roasting, smoking, stock
Nutrition (3 ounces cooked): 132 Cal, 22 g Prot, 5 g Total Fat, 2 g Sat Fat. 2 SmartPoints value

Thigh

Best for: Baking, braising, grilling, roasting, soups, stir-frying
Nutrition (4 ounce): 129 Cal, 22 g Prot, 5 g Total Fat, 1 g Sat Fat. 2 SmartPoints value

Poultry labeling: meaningful or just marketing?

The good news is that there's never been a wider range of terrific poultry options on the market. Even a midsize supermarket or a neighborhood butcher is bound to have a tremendous number of choices. But all those choices come with a number of descriptions, each with varying prices and differing claims about healthfulness, taste, and the welfare of the animals themselves. Here's a glossary of what to know before you buy.

Air-chilled

After processing, chicken is usually chilled rapidly in huge baths of ice water. Air-chilling uses cold air, not water, which has a few advantages: It reduces the risk of cross-contamination, prevents water absorption to protect natural flavor without increasing weight, and conserves water. Air-chilled chicken is usually more expensive than conventionally processed chicken, but remember that you won't be paying for excess water weight.

Antibiotic-free

Poultry raised in crowded conditions is particularly susceptible to disease, so antibiotics are often administered in feed as a preemptive measure. Critics of the practice cite the possible risks to humans from consuming "second-hand" antibiotics, in addition to the overuse of these medicines contributing to antibiotic-resistant bacterial strains ("superbugs") that could be a threat to public health.

Free-range

Poultry that's been given access to the outdoors for some time each day can be labeled "free-range" or "barn-roaming." The USDA does not specify conditions or length of time, leaving the term too broad to generalize whether the birds are exercising and foraging enough to significantly impact their quality of life or change the way they'll taste on your table.

Hormone-free

All poultry sold in the United States is required to be raised without added hormones, so any chicken you buy will be hormone-free (although this is not true of beef or dairy cows).

Humanely raised

There is currently no legal or USDA-sanctioned definition for what constitutes "humane" poultry practices. If you're concerned about animal treatment, it's best to focus on verified welfare standards, like how much space each chicken or turkey is allotted and whether perches are provided.

Kosher

Chicken or turkey prepared under rabbinical supervision can be labeled kosher. The process involves salting the bird; some salt is infused into the flesh (a benefit many cooks find extra tasty!), so additional brining of kosher birds is not recommended, and you may want to adjust the amount of additional salt you use when cooking.

Organic

To be labeled organic, poultry must be raised by USDA-certified organic practices, never treated with antibiotics, and given access to the outdoors. It must be raised on certified organic feed free of animal by-products and genetically modified grains. Organic chicken usually commands top dollar, but the standards are strict: A third-party inspector must visit the farm annually to make sure all requirements are met, so you can be sure you're getting a quality product that's raised in an ecological manner.

Pastured or pasture-raised

Although not a term recognized by the USDA, pastured chickens typically live outside as weather and daylight permit, enjoying fresh air and vegetation with the ability to engage in natural behaviors like scratching and foraging for insects. Farmers often use bottomless pens that are moved once or twice a day, providing the birds access to clean, new pasture as needed. Many cooks believe that these chickens' varied diet and increased muscle movement results in superior flavor.

White meat vs. dark meat

What's the difference? Quite a lot! These meats come from muscles that perform different jobs and result in different flavor, color, and texture.

White meat

Chicken and turkey breast meat is mild-flavored and tender, yet firm enough to carve into nice, even slices. It's lower in fat and calories than dark meat and that makes it terrific for anyone watching their weight, which is why it's a Weight Watchers zero Points food. But leanness has a downside, too: Breast meat can dry out rapidly during cooking. Watch it carefully and cook it with added fat if needed: a thin layer of olive oil in the bottom of a sauté pan, a coating of a marinade that contains oil, or even a wrapping of bacon or prosciutto for roasting. A moist-heat environment like poaching or steaming also helps white meat stay juicy. And although perfectly cooked white meat needs little more than salt and pepper, many diners appreciate a sauce or salsa to complement it.

Dark meat

The dark meat found in a bird's legs and thighs is darker due to a concentration of myoglobin, a chemical compound that helps oxygenation. Succulent and flavorful, dark meat has a slightly higher fat content than white meat, but it also has some advantages. Nutritionally, it beats white meat with higher concentrations of some vitamins and minerals, including B vitamins, iron, and zinc. And when it comes to flavor, dark meat is richer and more savory, and the higher fat content means it's less likely to dry out during cooking. You can make really tasty braises and grilled dishes with dark meat poultry in addition to roasting it at high temperatures. And note that although dark meat is an excellent choice for healthy eating, and a tastier choice for many recipes, it's higher fat and saturated fat content mean it's not a zero Points food.

Soft turkey tacos with smoky tomatillo salsa, page 68

Five tips for safety and freshness

Like all fresh meat, poultry is perishable so it should always be handled with care. Following a few easy safety rules will help eliminate the risk of foodborne illness from bacteria.

1. Keep chicken cold

Raw poultry should always be kept at a temperature of 40°F or less. Make sure it's the last thing you put in your cart when shopping, and never leave it in a hot car; an insulated bag or small cooler with a few ice packs will keep it safe on the trip home. And never leave cooked chicken or turkey out at room temperature for longer than 2 hours. Wrap leftovers and refrigerate as soon as possible after your meal.

2. Avoid cross-contamination

Raw poultry and its juices should be kept away from other foods. When shopping, place raw poultry in a plastic bag to ensure it doesn't leak on your groceries. For refrigeration, place chicken in its original packaging on a plate to prevent any juices from seeping out onto other foods. After preparing raw poultry, wash your hands, countertop, cutting boards, knives, and any utensils with hot, soapy water before they come in contact with other foods. Rinsing chicken in the sink is not recommended; it doesn't inhibit bacterial growth, and the process can splash juices around your kitchen and cause contamination.

3. Freeze after 2 days

Use raw poultry within 2 days or freeze it. You can store it in its original packaging for a few weeks, or overwrap the store packaging with heavy-duty aluminum foil, plastic wrap, or freezer paper. Or you can transfer portions to freezer-safe zip-close plastic bags, a good strategy if you want to be able to thaw portions like a single breast for easy meals. Always label the packages with the date and contents, and use within 9 months for best quality.

4. Thaw safely

The best and safest way to thaw poultry is in the refrigerator on a plate or rimmed tray to catch any juices. It takes about 24 hours in the fridge to thaw a whole 4-pound chicken, and 3 to 9 hours for parts. Allow 3 days to thaw a 12-pound turkey. Chicken can also be thawed in cold water: Place the chicken in its wrapping or in a zip-close plastic bag in a large bowl or pot of cold water, changing the water every 30 minutes to keep it cold. Although you can thaw chicken in a microwave according to the manufacturer's directions, it's not ideal; some areas will begin to cook while others stay raw. And you must cook the chicken immediately after microwaving to prevent bacterial growth.

5. Cook thoroughly

Poultry should be cooked to an internal temperature of at least 165°F for safety. Check the temperature with an instant-read thermometer at the thickest part of the meat not touching bone; on a whole bird, this is the thickest part of the thigh. A meat thermometer is a great investment, but if you don't have one you can pierce the chicken at its thickest point with the tip of a paring knife and then press the meat gently; the juices that run out should be clear, not pink. For a whole bird, the legs should move freely when it's cooked through, and any juices in the cavity should be clear.

Chicken and eggplant stir-fry with snow peas, page 125

Chapter 1

Quick chicken dinners in 20 minutes or less

Crispy chicken with red pepper sauce, 2

Cajun chicken with minty cucumber-tomato relish, 4

Chicken breast cutlets: the 8-minute dinner, 5

Indian-spiced chicken with mango raita, 7

Saffron and tomato chicken with olive couscous, 8

Chicken with creamy tarragon-mushroom sauce, 11

Chicken with tomatoes, apricots, and chickpeas, 12

Chicken with orange-avocado salsa, 13

Almond chicken cutlets with tangy cilantro slaw, 14

Parmesan chicken with fennel-arugula salad, 17

Grilled chicken salad with ginger-honey dressing, 18

Creamy chicken and corn chowder, 19

Asian chicken-mushroom soup, 20

Stir-fry chicken with cashews, 22

Chicken stir-fry with black bean sauce, 23

Chicken and asparagus stir-fry with basil, 25

Sautéed chicken thighs with lemon and capers, 26

Spicy farfalle with chicken chorizo and chickpeas, 27

Korean chicken and rice bowls, 28

Chicken sausages with bean-and-tomato salad, 31

Moroccan turkey and chickpea soup, 32

Penne with sausage, white beans, and kale, 33

Turkey-lentil curry, 34

Turkey tortilla wedges with arugula and pine nuts, 37

Orecchiette with sausage and broccoli rabe, 39

Crispy chicken with red pepper sauce

Gluten Free   Serves 4

Ready in minutes and made with pantry staples, this recipe will become a weeknight go-to. The sauce, a simple puree of roasted red peppers, balsamic vinegar, garlic, and basil, is delicious as a topping for pasta or salmon, too.

1	**(7-ounce) jar water-packed roasted red peppers, drained**
1	**tablespoon balsamic vinegar**
1	**garlic clove, chopped**
¾	**teaspoon salt**
4	**tablespoons chopped fresh basil**
1½	**tablespoons cornmeal**
½	**teaspoon black pepper**
4	**(5-ounce) skinless boneless chicken breasts**
2	**teaspoons olive oil**

1 Combine roasted peppers, vinegar, garlic, and ¼ teaspoon salt in blender or food processor; puree. Scrape mixture into small saucepan and set over medium heat. Cook, stirring often, until sauce just begins to simmer. Remove from heat and stir in 2 tablespoons basil. Keep warm.

2 Meanwhile, mix together cornmeal, remaining 2 tablespoons basil, remaining ½ teaspoon salt, and the black pepper in shallow dish. Add chicken breasts, one at a time, pressing lightly to coat.

3 Heat oil in large nonstick skillet over medium heat. Add chicken and cook, turning once, until chicken is browned and cooked through, about 8 minutes. Serve with sauce.

SmartPoints value per serving (1 chicken breast and 2 tablespoons sauce): 223 Cal, 6 g Total Fat, 1 g Sat Fat, 596 mg Sod, 9 g Total Carb, 2 g Sugar, 0 g Fib, 32 g Prot.

Freestyle it

Serve the chicken with a 0 SmartPoints value veggie that cooks in minutes. Steamed broccoli, green beans, spinach, asparagus, and cauliflower are all speedy and satisfying options.

**Crispy chicken with
red pepper sauce**

Cajun chicken with minty cucumber-tomato relish

Gluten Free **Serves 4**

Spearmint is the type of mint most commonly found in supermarkets and is perfect for this recipe. But if you can find other varieties like peppermint, lemon mint, or pineapple mint at specialty markets or farmers' markets, give them a try.

4	teaspoons olive oil
2	garlic cloves, minced
1	tablespoon paprika
2	teaspoons dried oregano
½	teaspoon red pepper flakes
1	teaspoon plus pinch black pepper
½	teaspoon plus pinch salt
4	(5-ounce) skinless boneless chicken breasts
1	cup plain fat-free yogurt
2	cups cherry tomatoes, quartered
½	large English (seedless) cucumber, diced
1	tablespoon thinly sliced fresh mint, plus additional for garnish

1 Stir together 2 teaspoons oil, the garlic, paprika, oregano, pepper flakes, 1 teaspoon black pepper, and ½ teaspoon salt in medium bowl. Add chicken and turn to coat.

2 Heat remaining 2 teaspoons oil in large nonstick skillet over medium heat. Add chicken and cook, turning once, until chicken is browned and cooked through, 8–10 minutes.

3 Meanwhile, to make relish, stir together yogurt, tomatoes, cucumber, 1 tablespoon mint, remaining pinch salt and remaining pinch pepper. Serve chicken with relish. Garnish with thinly sliced fresh mint.

 SmartPoints value per serving (1 chicken breast and about ⅓ cup relish): 271 Cal, 9 g Total Fat, 1 g Sat Fat, 477 mg Sod, 11 g Total Carb, 7 g Sugar, 2 g Fib, 36 g Prot.

Let's do this together
WW member Tracey Steckmeister says that planning meals for the week is absolutely essential to her success on the program. Here's a trick she uses for chicken recipes: "I buy chicken breasts in bulk, divide them into zip-close plastic bags according to the amount needed for the recipe I'm going to use them for, then label them with the recipe name and freeze."

Chicken breast cutlets: the 8-minute dinner

Here's a food that's easy to celebrate: boneless, skinless chicken breasts sliced horizontally into thin, even cutlets. They cook in a flash—around 8 minutes—and their uniform thickness means they cook more evenly. Our favorite part is that their increased surface area means there's more chicken to coat with flavorful rubs and marinades, and more exterior to brown and caramelize deliciously. Plus, they're a zero Points food, so you never have to track them.

Buy cutlets or slice your own

You can pick up a package of cutlets at just about any supermarket. They're often labeled as "thin-sliced chicken breast" or "thin chicken cutlets" (note that chicken known as "tenders" are a different part of the breast). But you can also easily make your own by following the simple steps below. If you have the time, pop the chicken breast in the freezer about 30 minutes before slicing it; the extra firmness will make it a little easier to split evenly.

1 Place a half skinless boneless chicken breast on a cutting board; 8 to 10 ounces is ideal. If you see a small strip of meat attached to the underside of the breast (it's known as a tender), remove it and save it for another use.

2 Lay one hand flat over the breast. With a sharp knife, slice through the breast horizontally until you have two thin, even pieces.

3 If there are thicker spots in your cutlets, lay a piece of plastic wrap or wax paper over the pieces and pound them gently with a rolling pin or the bottom of a small heavy skillet.

Cutlets to the rescue

Need a super-quick meal? We've used cutlets in recipes throughout this book, but keep these ideas in mind for meals in minutes.*

- See Magic with Rubs and Marinades on page 45 for easy flavoring ideas. Cutlets have lots of surface area to benefit from these delicious seasonings, and you can marinate them for just a few minutes and still get fantastic taste.

- Use cutlets in sandwiches and wraps. A simple sprinkle of salt and pepper and a spritz of cooking spray is all you need to grill or pan-sear them. They are excellent with mayo-based sauces, barbecue sauce, or sliced avocado and shredded veggies.

- Bread cutlets to make them wonderfully crisp and mouthwateringly juicy. Dredge the cutlets in flour seasoned with salt and pepper, dip in beaten egg, and coat in plain or seasoned bread crumbs or panko (Japanese bread crumbs). Pan-fry them in a thin layer of oil until golden brown.

- Keep some cooked cutlets in the fridge so you'll always have the basis for quick meals; they'll last for up to 3 days. Cut them in strips for fanning over salads or grain bowls, dice them for ramen or other hearty soups, or use them to make quick tacos or burritos.

*Serving suggestions may add SmartPoints. Consult your online calculator or our suggested rub and marinade recipes for specifics.

**Indian-spiced chicken
with mango raita**

Indian-spiced chicken with mango raita

Gluten Free   Serves 4

This minty raita, a sweet and crunchy blend of mango and cucumber, is equally delicious served with pork tenderloin, salmon, or shrimp. It makes a great 0 SmartPoints snack, too, when scooped up with jicama, carrot, or celery sticks.

½   **cup plain fat-free Greek yogurt**

1   **teaspoon grated peeled fresh ginger**

1   **teaspoon garam masala**

¾   **teaspoon salt**

¼   **teaspoon black pepper**

4   **(5-ounce) skinless boneless chicken breasts**

1   **teaspoon canola oil**

1   **ripe mango, peeled, pitted, and diced**

1   **Kirby cucumber, peeled and diced**

2   **tablespoons thinly sliced fresh mint**

Pinch cayenne

1 Whisk together ¼ cup yogurt, the ginger, garam masala, ½ teaspoon salt, and the pepper in medium bowl. Add chicken, turning to coat evenly.

2 Heat oil in large skillet over medium-high heat. Add chicken and cook, turning occasionally, until chicken is cooked through, 8–10 minutes.

3 Meanwhile, to make raita, stir together remaining ¼ cup yogurt, the mango, cucumber, mint, remaining ¼ teaspoon salt, and the cayenne in medium bowl. Serve chicken with raita.

0 **SmartPoints value per serving** (1 chicken breast and about ½ cup raita): 250 Cal, 5 g Total Fat, 1 g Sat Fat, 510 mg Sod, 15 g Total Carb, 13 g Sugar, 2 g Fib, 35 g Prot.

Saffron and tomato chicken with olive couscous

Serves 4

No saffron? No worries! You can skip this pricey spice and this dish will still be flavorful and delicious.

4   **(5-ounce) skinless boneless chicken breasts**
¼   **teaspoon salt**
¼   **teaspoon black pepper**
2   **teaspoons olive oil**
1   **(14½-ounce) can diced tomatoes**
2   **garlic cloves, minced**
¼   **teaspoon saffron threads, crumbled**
⅛   **teaspoon cinnamon**
2   **cups cooked whole wheat couscous**
¼   **cup quartered pitted Kalamata olives**
¼   **cup diced red onion**
3   **tablespoons sliced or slivered almonds, toasted**
2   **tablespoons chopped fresh flat-leaf parsley**

1 Sprinkle chicken with salt and pepper. Heat 1 teaspoon oil in large skillet over medium-high heat. Add chicken and cook, turning occasionally, until chicken is cooked through, 8–10 minutes. Transfer to plate.

2 Add tomatoes, garlic, saffron, and cinnamon to skillet; bring to boil. Reduce heat and simmer, stirring occasionally, until most of the liquid is evaporated, about 5 minutes. Return chicken to skillet.

3 Toss together couscous, olives, onion, almonds, parsley, and remaining 1 teaspoon oil in medium bowl.

4 Divide couscous evenly among 4 plates. Place chicken breasts alongside couscous; spoon tomato mixture evenly on top.

⑤ SmartPoints value per serving (1 chicken breast with ⅓ cup sauce and ½ cup couscous): 356 Cal, 10 g Total Fat, 2 g Sat Fat, 417 mg Sod, 30 g Total Carb, 4 g Sugar, 6 g Fib, 38 g Prot.

Let's do this together
WW member René Falgout's best tip for cooking skinless boneless chicken breasts—and we agree—is not to overcook them. "The safe internal temperature is 165°F," she says. "Cooking chicken breast beyond that is what leads to dry chicken."

Saffron and tomato chicken
with olive couscous

**Chicken with creamy
tarragon-mushroom sauce**

Chicken with creamy tarragon-mushroom sauce

Gluten Free   Serves 4

This classic quick-cooking chicken dish is layered with the flavors of mushrooms, wine, mustard, and garlic. Tarragon adds elegance to the sauce, but if you'd prefer, you can use fresh basil, thyme, or plain old parsley.

3	**teaspoons olive oil**
4	**(5-ounce) skinless boneless chicken breasts**
½	**teaspoon salt**
¼	**teaspoon black pepper**
2	**cups thinly sliced cremini mushrooms**
1	**garlic clove, minced**
¼	**cup dry white wine**
3	**tablespoons plain low-fat Greek yogurt**
2	**teaspoons Dijon mustard**
1½	**teaspoons chopped fresh tarragon**

1 Heat 2 teaspoons oil in large skillet over medium-high heat. Sprinkle chicken with ¼ teaspoon salt and ⅛ teaspoon pepper. Add chicken to skillet and cook, turning occasionally, until chicken is cooked through, 8–10 minutes. Transfer to plate; cover to keep warm.

2 Add remaining 1 teaspoon oil to skillet. Add mushrooms and garlic and cook, stirring often, until mushrooms are softened, about 5 minutes. Add wine and bring to boil. Cook until wine is slightly reduced, about 3 minutes. Remove pan from heat and stir in yogurt, mustard, tarragon, remaining ¼ teaspoon salt, and remaining ⅛ teaspoon pepper. Serve chicken with mushroom sauce.

2 **SmartPoints value per serving** (1 chicken breast with about ¼ cup mushrooms and sauce): 229 Cal, 7 g Total Fat, 1 g Sat Fat, 417 mg Sod, 2 g Total Carb, 1 g Sugar, 0 g Fib, 34 g Prot.

Chicken with tomatoes, apricots, and chickpeas

Gluten Free   Serves 4

This fresh and quick chicken stew makes a comforting meal in a hurry. If you don't have dried apricots, you can use raisins or dried cranberries. And if there's any cilantro or mint lurking in the fridge, sprinkle some onto each serving.

1	**teaspoon ground cumin**
1	**teaspoon ground coriander**
¾	**teaspoon salt**
¼	**teaspoon hot paprika**
4	**(5-ounce) skinless boneless chicken breasts**
3	**teaspoons olive oil**
1	**cup rinsed and drained canned chickpeas**
1	**(14½-ounce) can diced tomatoes with onion and garlic**
1	**large zucchini, quartered lengthwise and sliced ½-inch thick (about 2½ cups)**
⅓	**cup dried apricots, coarsely chopped**
	Lime wedges

1 Stir together cumin, coriander, salt, and paprika in small bowl. Rub chicken all over with spice mixture.

2 Heat 2 teaspoons oil in large skillet over medium-high heat. Add chicken and cook, turning once, until chicken is deep golden brown, about 8 minutes. Transfer chicken to plate.

3 Heat remaining 1 teaspoon oil in same skillet. Add chickpeas and cook, shaking pan, until chickpeas are browned, about 1 minute. Add tomatoes, zucchini, and apricots; bring to boil. Return chicken to skillet, nestling in tomato mixture, and return to boil.

4 Reduce heat and simmer, covered, until chicken is cooked through and zucchini is tender, about 5 minutes longer, turning chicken and stirring tomato mixture halfway through cooking time.

5 Divide evenly among 4 bowls; serve with lime wedges.

3 **SmartPoints value per serving** (1 chicken breast and 1 cup tomato mixture): 356 Cal, 9 g Total Fat, 1 g Sat Fat, 1,056 mg Sod, 29 g Total Carb, 14 g Sugar, 6 g Fib, 38 g Prot.

Chicken with orange-avocado salsa

Gluten Free   Serves 4

Thinner and quicker to cook than chicken breasts, chicken breast cutlets are a must-have for time-challenged weeknight cooks. Want to save a little money rather than time? See our easy technique for making your own cutlets on page 5.

4	**(5-ounce) skinless boneless chicken breast cutlets**
1	**teaspoon ground coriander**
½	**teaspoon plus ⅛ teaspoon salt**
¼	**teaspoon cayenne**
2	**teaspoons olive oil**
1	**navel orange, peeled and diced**
½	**Hass avocado, pitted, peeled, and diced**
2	**scallions, thinly sliced (white and light green parts only)**
2	**tablespoons chopped fresh cilantro**
½	**jalapeño pepper, seeded and minced**
2	**teaspoons fresh lime juice**
4	**lime wedges**

1 Sprinkle chicken with coriander, ½ teaspoon salt, and the cayenne. Heat oil in large skillet over medium-high heat. Add chicken and cook, turning once, until chicken is browned and cooked through, 6–8 minutes.

2 Meanwhile, to make salsa, stir together orange, avocado, scallions, cilantro, jalapeño, lime juice, and remaining ⅛ teaspoon salt in medium bowl. Serve chicken with salsa and lime wedges.

2 **SmartPoints value per serving** (1 chicken cutlet and ½ cup salsa): 254 Cal, 10 g Total Fat, 2 g Sat Fat, 430 mg Sod, 8 g Total Carb, 4 g Sugar, 3 g Fib, 33 g Prot.

Almond chicken cutlets with tangy cilantro slaw

Serves 4

Sprinkling the salt and chile powder directly on the cutlets instead of adding them to the bread-crumb mixture ensures that the seasonings stick to the chicken and guarantees you'll taste the chile in the finished dish.

¾ **cup panko (bread crumbs)**
¼ **cup ground almonds**
4 **(5-ounce) skinless boneless chicken breast cutlets**
¾ **teaspoon salt**
¼ **teaspoon ancho chile powder**
1 **large egg white, lightly beaten**
5 **teaspoons olive oil**
3 **tablespoons lime juice**
¼ **teaspoon black pepper**
4 **cups shredded red cabbage**
½ **cup chopped fresh cilantro**
Lime wedges

1 Mix together panko and almonds on sheet of wax paper. Sprinkle chicken with ½ teaspoon salt and the chile powder. Dip cutlets, one at a time, in egg white, then coat with panko mixture.

2 Heat 4 teaspoons oil in large nonstick skillet over medium heat. Add chicken and cook, turning once, until chicken is browned and cooked through, 6–8 minutes.

3 Meanwhile, stir together lime juice, remaining 1 teaspoon oil, remaining ¼ teaspoon salt, and the pepper in medium bowl. Add cabbage and cilantro; toss to coat. Serve chicken with slaw and lime wedges.

(5) **SmartPoints value per serving** (1 chicken cutlet and ¾ cup slaw): 357 Cal, 14 g Total Fat, 2 g Sat Fat, 655 mg Sod, 20 g Total Carb, 4 g Sugar, 3 g Fib, 37 g Prot.

Let's do this together

As a WW member for 20 years, Kathy Petrullo has found that planning her meals is the ultimate key to her success. "There is never a time when I don't have my meals and snacks planned and ready to go for the week," she says. "I'm an impulsive eater at times, and it's the only way I can stay on Plan."

Almond chicken cutlets
with tangy cilantro slaw

**Parmesan chicken with
fennel-arugula salad**

Parmesan chicken with fennel-arugula salad

Serves 4

1½ tablespoons lemon juice

1 tablespoon plus
1 teaspoon olive oil

¼ teaspoon honey or
agave nectar

¼ teaspoon salt

½ fennel bulb, trimmed
and thinly sliced

4 cups baby arugula

¼ cup plus 2 tablespoons
grated Parmesan

1 tablespoon dried seasoned
bread crumbs

4 (5-ounce) skinless boneless
chicken breast cutlets

1 Whisk together lemon juice, 1 tablespoon oil, the honey, and salt in large bowl. Place fennel on top, then add arugula; do not toss.

2 Combine ¼ cup Parmesan and the bread crumbs in small bowl. Place chicken on sheet of wax paper. Sprinkle half of Parmesan mixture evenly over one side of chicken breast cutlets and press to adhere.

3 Heat remaining 1 teaspoon oil in large nonstick skillet over medium heat. Add chicken, coated side down. Sprinkle remaining Parmesan mixture on top of chicken; lightly press to adhere. Cook, turning once, until chicken is lightly browned and cooked through, 6–8 minutes.

4 Toss together salad and dressing. Divide salad among 4 plates and top evenly with chicken. Sprinkle evenly with remaining 2 tablespoons Parmesan.

3 **SmartPoints value per serving** (1 chicken cutlet and ¾ cup salad): 270 Cal, 11 g Total Fat, 3 g Sat Fat, 423 mg Sod, 6 g Total Carb, 1 g Sugar, 1 g Fib, 35 g Prot.

Let's do this together

WW member Kathy Petrullo sprays a measuring spoon with nonstick spray before measuring sticky foods like honey, maple syrup, or peanut butter. It helps them easily release from the spoon, and as Kathy says, "It ensures that I get every last drop that I'm entitled to!"

Grilled chicken salad with ginger-honey dressing

Serves 4

1	**pound skinless boneless chicken breast cutlets**
½	**teaspoon salt**
¼	**teaspoon black pepper**
5	**ounces snow peas, trimmed and halved lengthwise**
4	**scallions, thinly sliced on diagonal**
3	**cups fresh bean sprouts**
½	**cup chopped fresh cilantro**
2	**tablespoons soy sauce**
4	**teaspoons canola oil**
1	**tablespoon grated peeled fresh ginger**
2	**teaspoons honey**
2	**teaspoons rice vinegar**
½	**teaspoon red pepper flakes**
2	**tablespoons unsalted dry-roasted peanuts, coarsely chopped**

1 Spray ridged grill pan with nonstick spray; set over medium-high heat until hot. Sprinkle chicken with salt and pepper. Add chicken to pan and cook, turning occasionally, until chicken is cooked through, 6–8 minutes. Transfer to cutting board.

2 Meanwhile, fill medium saucepan three-quarters full with water and bring to boil. Add snow peas and cook until crisp-tender, about 15 seconds. Drain. Rinse under cold running water until cool. Blot dry with paper towels.

3 Combine scallions, bean sprouts, cilantro, and snow peas in large bowl.

4 Whisk together soy sauce, oil, ginger, honey, vinegar, and pepper flakes in small bowl. Add half of soy sauce mixture to bean sprout mixture and toss to coat. Divide salad evenly among 4 plates. Slice chicken and arrange over salads. Drizzle evenly with remaining dressing. Sprinkle evenly with peanuts.

3 **SmartPoints value per serving** (1¼ cups salad and ½ tablespoon peanuts): 265 Cal, 10 g Total Fat, 1 g Sat Fat, 787 mg Sod, 13 g Total Carb, 8 g Sugar, 3 g Fib, 31 g Prot.

Let's do this together

Take an idea from WW member Dcgirl23 and add more protein and fiber to this recipe with cooked shelled edamame. "It's a surprisingly good flavor addition to chicken salad," she says.

Creamy chicken and corn chowder

Gluten Free   Serves 4

3   cups chicken broth

3   teaspoons olive oil

½   pound skinless boneless chicken breast, cut into ¾-inch cubes

½   teaspoon salt

¼   teaspoon black pepper

1   leek (white and light green parts only), halved lengthwise and thinly sliced

1   orange or yellow bell pepper, diced

¾   pound red-skinned potatoes, cut into ½-inch dice

3   sprigs fresh thyme, plus whole thyme leaves, for garnish

2   cups thawed frozen corn kernels

4   tablespoons plain low-fat Greek yogurt

¼   teaspoon red pepper flakes, or to taste

1 Add broth to medium saucepan and bring to boil over high heat.

2 Meanwhile, heat 2 teaspoons oil in large saucepan over medium-high heat. Sprinkle chicken with salt and black pepper. Add chicken to saucepan and cook, stirring often, until chicken is lightly browned, about 3 minutes. Transfer to plate.

3 Add remaining 1 teaspoon oil to same large saucepan. Add leek, bell pepper, potatoes, and thyme sprigs and cook, stirring often, until vegetables begin to soften, about 3 minutes.

4 Add hot broth to saucepan and bring to boil. Reduce heat, cover, and simmer until vegetables are almost tender, about 7 minutes. Add corn and chicken to saucepan and simmer until chicken is cooked through, about 2 minutes; remove from heat. Discard thyme sprigs. Stir in yogurt. (For a thicker soup, use a potato masher to mash some of the potatoes.)

5 Divide soup among 4 bowls and sprinkle with pepper flakes and thyme leaves.

4 **SmartPoints value per serving** (1½ cups): 304 Cal, 7 g Total Fat, 1 g Sat Fat, 893 mg Sod, 40 g Total Carb, 8 g Sugar, 5 g Fib, 23 g Prot.

Let's do this together

Plain fat-free Greek yogurt is a favorite ingredient for WW member René Falgout. "I'm a huge fan," she says. "I eat it with fruit, use it to make cucumber salad, as a base to make dips, and as a replacement for sour cream on baked potatoes, nachos, and chili. The possibilities are endless!"

Asian chicken-mushroom soup

Serves 4

Seasoned with ginger, star anise, five-spice powder, and soy sauce, this simple soup tastes like it simmered for hours. Brothy and veggie-packed, it's light enough to enjoy even when the weather is warm.

4	**(5-ounce) skinless boneless chicken breasts, cut into 1-inch pieces**
3	**cups chicken broth**
1	**cup water**
1	**teaspoon grated peeled fresh ginger**
2	**star anise**
¼	**teaspoon black pepper**
⅛	**teaspoon salt**
3	**scallions, cut into matchstick strips**
2	**bok choy, cut into 1-inch pieces**
5	**ounces cremini mushrooms, thinly sliced**
½	**teaspoon five-spice powder**
1	**tablespoon soy sauce**
2	**teaspoons mirin**

1 Combine chicken, broth, water, ginger, star anise, pepper, and salt in large saucepan. Cover and bring to boil over high heat. Reduce heat and simmer, covered, until chicken is almost cooked through, about 2 minutes.

2 Add three-quarters of scallions, the bok choy, mushrooms, and five-spice powder. Return to simmer and cook, covered, until vegetables are crisp-tender, about 3 minutes.

3 Remove from heat and stir in soy sauce and mirin. Discard star anise. Ladle soup into 4 bowls and top evenly with remaining scallions.

1 **SmartPoints value per serving** (1¾ cups): 279 Cal, 6 g Total Fat, 1 g Sat Fat, 1,190 mg Sod, 14 g Total Carb, 6 g Sugar, 5 g Fib, 44 g Prot.

Cook's tip

Star anise is a tiny fruit that grows on a short tree in China and Japan. When used whole and removed from a dish, as in this recipe, it imparts its licorice taste with a light touch, adding a mysterious layer of flavor.

Asian chicken-mushroom soup

Stir-fry chicken with cashews

Serves 4

The spice blend in this stir-fry, using star anise and fennel seeds, gives the dish licorice-like flavor. If this isn't your favorite taste, you can leave these out and the dish will still be delicious.

- **2 tablespoons soy sauce**
- **1 tablespoon rice wine**
- **1 tablespoon cider vinegar**
- **2 teaspoons packed brown sugar**
- **4 teaspoons peanut or canola oil**
- **3 garlic cloves, lightly smashed**
- **1 tablespoon grated peeled fresh ginger**
- **2 teaspoons Szechuan peppercorns, crushed**
- **1 teaspoon fennel seeds, crushed**
- **1 star anise**
- **1 pound skinless boneless chicken breast, cut into ½-inch cubes**
- **¼ teaspoon salt**
- **1 large orange bell pepper, sliced**
- **1 medium red onion, sliced**
- **¼ cup chopped fresh cilantro**
- **¼ cup roasted cashews, coarsely chopped**

1 Stir together soy sauce, rice wine, vinegar, and brown sugar in small bowl.

2 Heat large deep skillet or wok over high heat until drop of water sizzles in pan. Add 2 teaspoons oil and swirl to coat pan. Add garlic, ginger, peppercorns, fennel seeds, and star anise and stir-fry until fragrant, about 15 seconds. Add chicken in one layer, sprinkle with salt, and cook, without stirring, 1 minute. Then stir-fry until chicken is no longer pink, 1–2 minutes. Transfer chicken mixture to bowl.

3 Heat remaining 2 teaspoons oil in pan. Add bell pepper and onion and stir-fry until vegetables are crisp-tender, 1–2 minutes. Add chicken and soy sauce mixtures. Cook, stirring often, until chicken is heated through, about 1 minute. Sprinkle with cilantro and cashews. Remove garlic and star anise before serving.

 SmartPoints value per serving (1 cup): 282 Cal, 12 g Total Fat, 2 g Sat Fat, 658 mg Sod, 15 g Total Carb, 7 g Sugar, 2 g Fib, 29 g Prot.

Cook's tip
Szechuan peppercorns aren't technically peppers but dried fruit husks from a Chinese prickly ash tree. These tiny husks have a light citrusy flavor and piney aroma. If you don't like Szechuan peppercorns, substitute 1 teaspoon crushed coriander seeds and ½ teaspoon cracked black pepper.

Chicken stir-fry with black bean sauce

Serves 4

Whether you're using pea shoots, watercress, or baby spinach in this stir-fry, add it after removing the skillet from the heat to ensure that it retains its vibrant color and fresh flavor.

¾ **pound skinless boneless chicken breast, cut into thin strips**

¼ **teaspoon salt**

¼ **teaspoon black pepper**

3 **teaspoons Asian (dark) sesame oil**

2 **red, orange, or yellow bell peppers, thinly sliced**

1 **large shallot, halved and thinly sliced**

2 **garlic cloves, minced**

⅓ **cup water**

¼ **cup Asian black bean sauce**

1 **teaspoon soy sauce**

1½ **cups lightly packed pea shoots, watercress, or baby spinach**

2 **teaspoons toasted sesame seeds**

1 Sprinkle chicken with salt and black pepper. Heat large skillet or wok over medium-high heat until drop of water sizzles in pan. Add 2 teaspoons oil and swirl to coat pan. Add chicken and cook, without stirring, 1 minute. Then stir-fry until chicken is cooked through, about 3 minutes. Transfer chicken to plate.

2 Add remaining 1 teaspoon oil to skillet. Add bell peppers, shallot, and garlic and cook, stirring often, until vegetables begin to soften, 2–3 minutes. Stir in water, black bean sauce, and soy sauce and cook until mixture comes to boil, about 1 minute. Return chicken to skillet. Remove from heat and add pea shoots; gently toss just until wilted, about 15 seconds. Sprinkle with sesame seeds.

2 **SmartPoints value per serving** (1 cup): 201 Cal, 8 g Total Fat, 1 g Sat Fat, 614 mg Sod, 9 g Total Carb, 3 g Sugar, 3 g Fib, 23 g Prot.

Let's do this together
Want to speed up your time in the kitchen? Take a tip from WW member swarner196 and consider a knife-skills class. "I took one at a cookware store," she explains. "I learned so many shortcuts that have saved me time and energy. Now people tell me I can cut a bell pepper like a ninja!"

Chicken and asparagus stir-fry with basil

Chicken and asparagus stir-fry with basil

Serves 4

¾	**cup chicken broth**
3	**tablespoons soy sauce**
1	**tablespoon cornstarch**
4	**teaspoons canola oil**
1	**pound skinless boneless chicken breast cutlets, cut into thin strips**
¼	**teaspoon salt**
¼	**teaspoon black pepper**
2	**garlic cloves, minced**
1	**tablespoon minced peeled fresh ginger**
1	**pound thin asparagus, trimmed and cut into 1-inch pieces**
1	**small red or yellow bell pepper, thinly sliced**
2	**scallions, cut into 1-inch pieces**
¼	**cup fresh basil leaves**
1	**tablespoon sesame seeds**

1 Whisk together broth, soy sauce, and cornstarch in small bowl until smooth.

2 Heat large skillet or wok over medium-high heat until drop of water sizzles in pan. Add 2 teaspoons oil and swirl to coat pan. Add chicken, sprinkle with salt and pepper, and cook, without stirring, 1 minute. Then stir-fry until chicken is cooked through, about 3 minutes. Transfer chicken to plate.

3 Heat remaining 2 teaspoons oil in same pan. Add garlic and ginger and stir-fry until fragrant, 30 seconds. Add asparagus, bell pepper, and scallions; stir-fry until vegetables are crisp-tender, about 3 minutes. Return chicken to pan. Whisk broth mixture again and add to pan. Cook, stirring constantly, until mixture bubbles and thickens, about 1 minute. Remove from heat and stir in basil. Sprinkle with sesame seeds.

2 **SmartPoints value per serving** (1½ cups): 243 Cal, 9 g Total Fat, 1 g Sat Fat, 995 mg Sod, 10 g Total Carb, 3 g Sugar, 3 g Fib, 31 g Prot.

Cook's tip
Instead of asparagus, you can make this stir-fry with 3 cups of small broccoli florets, sugar snap peas, or cubed eggplant.

Sautéed chicken thighs with lemon and capers

Serves 4

Classic for a reason, chicken with a tart and salty sauce of lemon and capers is simplicity at its most delicious. This version is made with chicken thighs, which taste richer and more complex than breasts.

4 **(5-ounce) skinless boneless chicken thighs**
¼ **teaspoon salt**
¼ **teaspoon black pepper**
¼ **cup all-purpose flour**
1 **teaspoon olive oil**
1 **large shallot, chopped**
1 **cup chicken broth**
1 **teaspoon grated lemon zest**
2 **tablespoons lemon juice**
1½ **tablespoons capers, drained**
Chopped fresh parsley or chives, for garnish (optional)
Lemon wedges

1 Sprinkle chicken with salt and pepper. Place flour in large bowl. Add chicken and turn until coated evenly.

2 Heat oil in large nonstick skillet over medium heat. Place chicken in skillet and cook until chicken is golden on bottom, about 6 minutes. Turn and cook until cooked through, about 4 minutes longer. Transfer chicken to plate and keep warm.

3 Add shallot to skillet and cook, stirring often, until shallot is softened, about 3 minutes. Add broth and cook, stirring with wooden spoon to scrape up browned bits from bottom of pan. Stir in lemon zest and juice and capers; cook 30 seconds longer.

4 Place 1 chicken thigh on each of 4 plates; top evenly with sauce. Sprinkle with parsley, if using. Serve with lemon wedges.

 SmartPoints value per serving (1 chicken thigh and about 3 tablespoons sauce): 232 Cal, 7 g Total Fat, 2 g Sat Fat, 545 mg Sod, 9 g Total Carb, 1 g Sugar, 1 g Fib, 30 g Prot.

Spicy farfalle with chicken chorizo and chickpeas

Serves 4

This is an incredibly versatile pasta dish. Make it with any shape of short pasta, swap in Italian turkey sausage, try baby spinach or arugula instead of kale, and use cannellini, navy, or borlotti beans for the chickpeas.

6	**ounces farfalle (bowtie) pasta**
2	**teaspoons olive oil**
6	**ounces chorizo-style chicken sausages, split lengthwise and cut into ¼-inch slices**
4	**cups baby kale**
2	**cups grape tomatoes, halved**
1	**(15-ounce) can chickpeas, rinsed and drained**
3	**scallions, thinly sliced**
2	**garlic cloves, minced**
½	**teaspoon salt**
⅛	**teaspoon red pepper flakes**

1 Cook pasta according to package directions.

2 Meanwhile, heat oil in 12-inch skillet over medium-high heat. Add sausage and cook, stirring occasionally, until sausage is lightly browned, about 2 minutes.

3 Add kale and cook until wilted, about 1 minute. Add tomatoes, chickpeas, scallions, garlic, salt, and pepper flakes, and cook, stirring often, just until heated through, about 1 minute.

4 Add pasta to skillet and toss to combine.

7 **SmartPoints value per serving** (1¾ cups): 430 Cal, 10 g Total Fat, 2 g Sat Fat, 888 mg Sod, 63 g Total Carb, 9 g Sugar, 9 g Fib, 22 g Prot.

Cook's tip
Always weigh dry pasta before cooking. Even experienced cooks are not good at "guesstimating," and the SmartPoints add up fast if you're off by just an ounce or two.

Korean chicken and rice bowls

Serves 4

We all wanted seconds of this flavor-packed meal when we tried it at the office. It's a winner: fast, supereasy, low in SmartPoints, and delicious!

2   **teaspoons Asian (dark) sesame oil**

1   **onion, finely chopped**

2   **garlic cloves, minced**

1   **pound ground skinless chicken breast**

¼   **teaspoon salt**

2   **large carrots, shredded**

⅓   **cup chicken broth**

2   **tablespoons gochujang (Korean hot pepper paste)**

2   **tablespoons soy sauce**

⅓   **cup chopped fresh cilantro**

1   **(8.8-ounce) package ready-cook brown rice, microwaved according to package directions (1¾ cups)**

1   **English (seedless) cucumber, halved lengthwise and thinly sliced**

Red pepper flakes (optional)

Lime wedges

1 Heat large deep skillet or wok over medium-high heat until drop of water sizzles in pan. Add oil and swirl to coat pan. Add onion and garlic and stir-fry until onion softens, 1–2 minutes.

2 Sprinkle chicken with salt and add to pan with carrots. Stir-fry until chicken is no longer pink, about 3 minutes.

3 Add broth, gochujang, and soy sauce. Bring to boil, stir-frying with wooden spoon to scrape up browned bits from bottom of pan. Remove pan from heat and stir in cilantro.

4 Divide rice evenly among 4 bowls; top evenly with chicken mixture and cucumber. Sprinkle with red pepper flakes, if using. Serve with lime wedges.

 SmartPoints value per serving (1 cup chicken mixture and about ⅓ cup rice): 304 Cal, 6 g Total Fat, 1 g Sat Fat, 790 mg Sod, 31 g Total Carb, 6 g Sugar, 3 g Fib, 30 g Prot.

Cook's tip
Gochujang is a staple in Korean cooking—and for good reason: Its sweet heat is fabulous on everything from chicken to vegetables. Heat levels can vary among brands, so check the packaging to see if it's labeled with any kind of spice-level indicator.

**Korean chicken
and rice bowls**

**Chicken sausages with warm
bean-and-tomato salad**

Chicken sausages with bean-and-tomato salad

Gluten Free   **Serves 4**

This fresh take on chicken sausages pairs them with a colorful lemon-dressed salad of green beans, lima beans, and cherry tomatoes, all tossed with fresh chives and mint.

1	**pound sweet Italian or other fresh chicken sausages (about 3 sausage links)**
½	**pound cherry tomatoes, halved**
½	**pound Italian flat beans or green beans, trimmed and halved crosswise**
1	**tablespoon extra-virgin olive oil**
½	**teaspoon grated lemon zest**
2	**teaspoons lemon juice**
1	**teaspoon Dijon mustard**
1	**large garlic clove, crushed through a press**
¼	**teaspoon salt, or to taste**
¼	**teaspoon black pepper**
1	**(15-ounce) can lima or cannellini (white kidney) beans, rinsed and drained**
2	**tablespoons chopped fresh chives**
1	**tablespoon chopped fresh mint**

1 Preheat broiler. Line broiler rack with foil; spray foil with nonstick spray.

2 Arrange sausages on foil in single layer. Broil 4 inches from heat until sausages are browned on top, about 8 minutes. Turn and broil 4 minutes longer. Add tomatoes to broiler rack. Return to broiler and broil until sausages are cooked through and tomatoes begin to soften, about 3 minutes.

3 Meanwhile, bring medium saucepan filled three-quarters full with lightly salted water to boil. Add green beans and cook until crisp-tender, about 3 minutes. Drain.

4 Whisk together oil, lemon zest and juice, mustard, garlic, salt, and pepper in large bowl. Add green beans, lima beans, tomatoes, chives, and mint and toss to combine. Cut sausages into ½-inch slices and serve with salad.

5 **SmartPoints value per serving** (¼ of sausage and 1 cup salad): 314 Cal, 12 g Total Fat, 3 g Sat Fat, 1,081 mg Sod, 25 g Total Carb, 2 g Sugar, 8 g Fib, 29 g Prot.

Moroccan turkey and chickpea soup

Gluten Free   Serves 4

2	teaspoons olive oil
1	small onion, finely chopped
4	ounces baby spinach
2½	cups chicken broth
1	(14½-ounce) can diced tomatoes, drained
1	cup thawed frozen green peas
1	(15-ounce) can chickpeas, rinsed and drained
4	teaspoons harissa
2	cups diced cooked skinless turkey breast
¼	teaspoon salt
¼	teaspoon black pepper

Lemon wedges

1 Heat oil in large saucepan over medium-high heat. Add onion and cook, covered, stirring occasionally, until it begins to soften, about 3 minutes. Add spinach and cook, stirring constantly, just until wilted, about 1 minute. Add broth, tomatoes, green peas, half of chickpeas, and the harissa and bring to boil.

2 Remove saucepan from heat. Coarsely puree soup using immersion blender or regular blender.

3 Return saucepan to medium-high heat. Add turkey and remaining chickpeas and simmer until heated through, about 2 minutes. Stir in salt and pepper.

4 Ladle into 4 bowls and serve with lemon wedges.

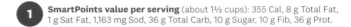

1 **SmartPoints value per serving** (about 1½ cups): 355 Cal, 8 g Total Fat, 1 g Sat Fat, 1,163 mg Sod, 36 g Total Carb, 10 g Sugar, 10 g Fib, 36 g Prot.

Let's do this together

Take a shopping tip from WW member René Falgout: As she shops, she keeps similar items together in the cart. At checkout, they go onto the conveyor in the same groups to get bagged together. "This makes it easier to unload the groceries and organize the pantry and refrigerator when I get home," she says.

Penne with sausage, white beans, and kale

Serves 6

Spicy turkey sausage is what gives this streamlined pasta-and-bean supper its hearty flavor. Add kale for texture and color and you've got comfort food at its delicious, nutritious best.

½ **pound penne**

2 **teaspoons olive oil**

½ **pound hot Italian turkey sausages, casings removed**

1 **(¾-pound) bunch kale, stems removed and leaves coarsely chopped**

1 **(14½-ounce) can chicken broth**

4 **plum tomatoes, diced**

¼ **teaspoon salt**

¼ **teaspoon black pepper**

1 **(15½-ounce) can cannellini (white kidney) beans, rinsed and drained**

¼ **cup grated Parmesan**

¼ **cup chopped fresh basil**

1 Cook penne according to package directions.

2 Meanwhile, heat oil in 12-inch nonstick skillet over medium heat. Add sausage and cook, breaking it apart with wooden spoon, until sausage is no longer pink, about 5 minutes. Add kale in batches, the broth, tomatoes, salt, and pepper; bring to boil. Reduce heat and simmer until kale starts to wilt, about 4 minutes. Add beans and simmer, uncovered, about 5 minutes longer.

3 Add pasta to skillet. Cook, stirring occasionally, until well mixed, about 1 minute. Serve sprinkled with Parmesan and basil.

 7 **SmartPoints value per serving** (1 cup pasta mixture and 2 teaspoons cheese): 335 Cal, 7 g Total Fat, 2 g Sat Fat, 879 mg Sod, 46 g Total Carb, 4 g Sugar, 6 g Fib, 21 g Prot.

Cook's tip

To quickly strip the leaves from kale, Swiss chard, or collards, work with one leaf at a time and hold it by the stem. Using the thumb and forefinger of the other hand, pinch the stem and pull down to easily remove the leaf.

Turkey-lentil curry

Gluten Free   Serves 4

3   teaspoons olive oil

1   **onion, halved and thinly sliced**

¾   **pound ground skinless turkey breast**

2   **garlic cloves, crushed**

1   **tablespoon garam masala**

½   **teaspoon ground turmeric**

½   **teaspoon chili powder**

½   **teaspoon ground cumin**

1   **(14½-ounce) can diced tomatoes**

1   **(15-ounce) can lentils, rinsed and drained**

1   **cup water**

½   **teaspoon salt**

4   **tablespoons plain fat-free yogurt**

Fresh mint leaves

1 Heat 2 teaspoons oil in large skillet over medium-high heat. Add onion; cover and cook, stirring occasionally, until onion is softened, about 3 minutes. Add remaining 1 teaspoon oil. Add turkey and cook, breaking it apart with wooden spoon, until turkey is no longer pink, about 2 minutes.

2 Add garlic, garam masala, turmeric, chili powder, and cumin and cook, stirring constantly, until fragrant, 30 seconds. Add tomatoes, lentils, water, and salt and bring to boil, stirring with wooden spoon to scrape up browned bits from bottom of pan. Reduce heat and simmer 3 minutes.

3 Ladle evenly into 4 bowls and top evenly with yogurt. Sprinkle with mint.

1 **SmartPoints value per serving** (generous 1½ cups curry and 1 tablespoon yogurt): 290 Cal, 6 g Total Fat, 1 g Sat Fat, 506 mg Sod, 30 g Total Carb, 7 g Sugar, 10 g Fib, 32 g Prot.

Cook's tip
Canned lentils are a fantastic zero Points pantry staple. Their mild earthy flavor makes them perfect for soups and salads and they're an easy way to get in some fiber— ½ cup has 8 grams!

Turkey-lentil curry

Turkey tortilla wedges with arugula and pine nuts

Turkey tortilla wedges with arugula and pine nuts

Serves 4

Sumac, made from the dried and ground berries of the sumac bush, is a common spice in Middle Eastern cooking. It lends a tart, slightly acidic flavor to this dish.

4	**(8-inch) flour tortillas**
4	**teaspoons olive oil**
¾	**pound ground skinless turkey breast**
¼	**teaspoon salt**
1	**large shallot, halved and thinly sliced**
2	**large garlic cloves, minced**
1	**cup cherry tomatoes, quartered**
2	**teaspoons ground sumac**
1	**teaspoon tomato paste**
⅓	**cup water**
⅓	**cup crumbled feta**
3	**tablespoons chopped fresh cilantro**
½	**cup baby arugula**
2	**tablespoons toasted pine nuts**
	Lemon wedges

1 Preheat oven to 400°F.

2 Place tortillas on large baking sheet in single layer and brush tops with 1 teaspoon oil. Bake until crisp, about 8 minutes.

3 Meanwhile, heat 2 teaspoons oil in large skillet over medium-high heat. Add turkey and salt; cook, stirring occasionally, until turkey is no longer pink, about 2 minutes. Add remaining 1 teaspoon oil to skillet. Add shallot and garlic and cook, stirring often, until shallot is softened, about 2 minutes. Add tomatoes, sumac, and tomato paste and cook, stirring constantly, 1 minute. Stir in water and cook, stirring with wooden spoon to scrape up browned bits from bottom of pan, about 1 minute. Remove from heat; stir in feta and cilantro.

4 Top tortillas evenly with turkey mixture, then top evenly with arugula and pine nuts. Cut each tortilla into 4 wedges. Serve with lemon wedges.

 SmartPoints value per serving (4 wedges): 369 Cal, 15 g Total Fat, 4 g Sat Fat, 859 mg Sod, 31 g Total Carb, 5 g Sugar, 3 g Fib, 27 g Prot.

Let's do this together

If you have trouble with self-control at the supermarket, WW member Kshatriya Millick has a brilliant shopping strategy. "I go shopping after my Weight Watchers meeting," she says. "I feel motivated and more relaxed after my meeting, so I'm a smarter shopper."

Orecchiette with
sausage and
broccoli rabe

Orecchiette with sausage and broccoli rabe

Serves 6

Sweet and juicy grape tomatoes offset the slightly bitter flavor of broccoli rabe in this quick, hearty pasta dish. Italian turkey sausage is a healthy and low-SmartPoints option to traditional pork sausage—and it's just as flavorful.

8   ounces orecchiette pasta

1   **bunch (1¼ pounds) broccoli rabe, trimmed and chopped**

¾   **pound Italian turkey sausages, casings removed**

2   **garlic cloves, thinly sliced**

½   **teaspoon red pepper flakes**

1   **cup grape tomatoes, halved**

2   **tablespoons white-wine vinegar**

½   **teaspoon salt**

¼   **cup finely shredded Romano**

1 Bring large pot of lightly salted water to boil. Add pasta and cook 4 minutes. Add broccoli rabe and cook until pasta and greens are just tender, about 5 minutes longer. Drain, reserving ¼ cup cooking water.

2 Meanwhile, cook sausage in large nonstick skillet over medium heat, breaking it apart with wooden spoon, until sausage is no longer pink, about 4 minutes. Add garlic and pepper flakes and cook, stirring constantly, until fragrant, 30 seconds. Add tomatoes, reserved cooking water, vinegar, and salt and cook, stirring with wooden spoon to scrape up browned bits from bottom of pan, just until tomatoes are heated through, about 1 minute. Add pasta mixture to skillet and stir to combine. Divide pasta evenly among 6 bowls. Sprinkle evenly with Romano.

 6 **SmartPoints value per serving** (generous 1 cup pasta mixture and 2 teaspoons cheese): 260 Cal, 7 g Total Fat, 2 g Sat Fat, 636 mg Sod, 33 g Total Carb, 2 g Sugar, 4 g Fib, 17 g Prot.

Cook's tip
Broccoli rabe, also called rapini, looks like leafy broccoli. It is sturdier than regular broccoli and has a slightly bitter flavor. To prepare it, trim away the large tough stems, leaving the slender stems, leaves, and florets.

Chapter 2

Dinner on the grill

Brown sugar–brined chicken, 42
Magic with rubs and marinades, 45
   Basic spice rub, 45
   Montreal chicken rub, 45
   Coffee rub, 45
   Basic lemon-herb marinade, 45
   Peruvian chicken marinade, 45
   Indian-spiced yogurt marinade, 45
Mojito barbecued chicken, 46
Chicken and corn salad with yogurt-lime dressing, 47
Chicken with tomato-zucchini salad, 48
Chicken with couscous-mango salad, 50
Chicken packets with zucchini and tomatoes, 51
Chicken with cucumber, orange, and olive salad, 53
Grilled chicken with tomato-anchovy sauce, 54
Asian chicken with carrot-cucumber slaw, 55
Grilled chicken with shishito peppers, 56
Chicken with grapefruit-mint salsa, 59
Chicken with tomato, olive, and feta salad, 60
Vietnamese chicken thighs with mango relish, 61
Chicken and veggie kebabs with romesco sauce, 62
Chicken with orange and basil gremolata, 64
Moroccan-style chicken with olives, 65
Grilled chicken with cucumber and herb salad, 67
Soft turkey tacos with smoky tomatillo salsa, 68
Grilled turkey tacos with strawberry salsa, 70
Turkey cutlets with couscous-cucumber salad, 71
Grilled turkey with watermelon and herb salad, 73
Grilled sausage and onion salad with figs, 75

Brown sugar-brined chicken

Gluten Free   Serves 6

Starting with a cut-up chicken instead of a whole bird makes brining so easy—and the results are so flavorful and moist—that you might make a habit of it!

4   **cups cold water**

½   **cup packed light brown sugar**

⅓   **cup kosher salt**

1   **whole cut-up chicken (about 3½ pounds)**

1   **small onion, thinly sliced**

4   **garlic cloves, chopped**

3   **bay leaves**

2   **teaspoons whole peppercorns**

1 Combine water, brown sugar, and salt in large bowl; whisk until salt and sugar dissolve.

2 Place chicken, onion, garlic, bay leaves, and peppercorns in large heavy-duty zip-close plastic bag. Add water mixture. Squeeze out air and seal bag; turn to coat chicken. Place bag inside large bowl. Refrigerate at least 8 hours or up to 12 hours. Remove chicken from brining solution and pat dry. Discard brining solution.

3 Spray ridged grill pan with nonstick spray and set over medium heat.

4 Place chicken in pan and grill, turning occasionally, until chicken is cooked through, 30–35 minutes. Remove skin before eating.

(3) **SmartPoints value per serving** (⅙ of chicken): 176 Cal, 4 g Total Fat, 1 g Sat Fat, 650 mg Sod, 5 g Total Carb, 3 g Sugar, 0 g Fib, 28 g Prot.

Brown sugar–brined chicken

Indian-spiced yogurt marinade

Coffee rub

Montreal chicken rub

Basic lemon-herb marinade

Peruvian chicken marinade

Basic spice rub

Magic with rubs and marinades

Marinades tenderize proteins with acids and oils, and rubs help foods develop a delicious crust. Both and add great flavor and give you the kind of irresistible aromas that everyone craves from grilling. Here are some tips for rubbing and marinating poultry for grilled perfection.

- Most of the benefits of marinating occur in the first few hours. It's often easiest to marinate overnight, but even 20 minutes will give you good flavor results and protect the surface of your food from drying out.

- If you're using a dry rub, let the rub sit on your food for at least a few minutes, but a few hours will help it penetrate better. Although the salt in rubs helps infuse flavorings into poultry, it can dry out the surface of the meat if left on for too long.

- Increasing the surface area of your food will boost the impact of rubs and marinades. For boneless breasts, pounding them lightly or using thin-cut cutlets is a good idea. For whole birds, spatchcocking (removing the backbone so the bird can lie flat) opens up all surfaces, inside and out, for coating.

- If you're cooking poultry with the skin on, try working some dry rub under the skin for maximum impact.

- Always discard any marinade after you remove your meat unless your recipe directs otherwise.

Easy dry rubs

Use about 1 tablespoon of rub per pound of chicken, or 1 teaspoon for each 4- to 6-ounce thigh or skinless boneless breast. Sprinkle the mixture over the meat and gently massage it in with your fingers. Let it sit for a few minutes, or cover and refrigerate chicken breasts or thighs for up to 4 hours and bone-in chicken pieces up to overnight. Store leftover rub in an airtight jar for up to 2 months.

Basic spice rub
(Makes ⅓ cup, about 16 servings)
Stir together 1 tablespoon chili powder, 1 tablespoon ground cumin, 1 tablespoon paprika, 1 tablespoon sugar, 2 teaspoons dried oregano, 2 teaspoons garlic powder, 2 teaspoons onion powder, and 2 teaspoons kosher salt.
Per serving (1 teaspoon): SmartPoints value: 0

Montreal chicken rub
(Makes ¼ cup, about 12 servings)
Stir together 2 teaspoons coarse sea salt, 1½ teaspoons cracked black pepper, 1½ teaspoons dried minced onion, ¾ teaspoon red pepper flakes, ¾ teaspoon dried thyme, ¾ teaspoon dried rosemary, ¾ teaspoon crushed coriander seeds, and ½ teaspoon dried minced garlic.
Per serving (1 teaspoon): SmartPoints value: 0

Coffee rub
(Makes ⅓ cup, about 16 servings)
Stir together 1½ tablespoons finely ground coffee, 1½ tablespoons brown sugar, 2 teaspoons kosher salt, 1 teaspoon chili powder, and ⅛ teaspoon cayenne.
Per serving (1 teaspoon): SmartPoints value: 0

Marinades

Use about 2 tablespoons per pound of chicken, or 1 tablespoon for each 4- or 5-ounce thigh or skinless boneless breast. Place the meat in a zip-close plastic bag and add the marinade. Squeeze out air, seal the bag, and turn to coat the chicken. Refrigerate chicken breasts or thighs for up to 4 hours and bone-in chicken pieces up to overnight.

Basic lemon-herb marinade
(Makes ⅓ cup, about 5 servings)
Whisk together 2 tablespoons olive oil, 3 cloves minced garlic, finely grated zest of 1 lemon, 2 tablespoons lemon juice, 1 tablespoon chopped thyme, 2 teaspoons chopped rosemary, 1 teaspoon salt, and ¾ teaspoon ground black pepper.
Per serving (1 tablespoon): SmartPoints value: 2

Peruvian chicken marinade
(Makes ⅓ cup, about 5 servings)
Whisk together 2 tablespoons soy sauce, 1 tablespoon white-wine vinegar, 1 tablespoon canola oil, 3 cloves minced garlic, 1 teaspoon ground cumin, 1 teaspoon paprika, ¾ teaspoon dried oregano, ½ teaspoon salt, and large pinch cayenne.
Per serving (1 tablespoon): SmartPoints value: 1

Indian-spiced yogurt marinade
(Makes generous ¾ cup, about 12 servings)
Whisk together ¾ cup plain fat-free yogurt (not Greek), 2 tablespoons olive oil, 2 tablespoons fresh lime juice, 3 cloves minced garlic, 2 teaspoons peeled minced fresh ginger, 2 teaspoons garam masala, 1½ teaspoons salt, ½ teaspoon ground turmeric, ½ teaspoon black pepper, and ⅛ teaspoon cayenne.
Per serving (generous 1 tablespoon): SmartPoints value: 1

Mojito barbecued chicken

Gluten Free   Serves 6

Buying a whole chicken already cut up is worth it for the convenience and time saved. The whole pieces are a nice change from skinless boneless chicken breasts, and some cooks believe that cooking chicken on the bone makes the meat more flavorful.

2   **tablespoons grated lime zest**

¼   **cup lime juice**

¼   **cup orange juice**

2   **tablespoons chopped fresh mint**

1   **tablespoon honey**

2   **garlic cloves, minced**

2   **teaspoons olive oil**

1   **teaspoon ground cumin**

¾   **teaspoon salt**

¼   **teaspoon black pepper**

1   **whole cut-up chicken (about 3½ pounds)**

Lime wedges

1 To make marinade, whisk together lime zest and juice, orange juice, mint, honey, garlic, oil, cumin, salt, and pepper in small bowl. Transfer half of lime mixture to covered container and refrigerate. Transfer remaining lime mixture into large zip-close plastic bag and add chicken. Squeeze out air and seal bag; turn to coat chicken. Refrigerate, turning bag occasionally, at least 2 hours or up to overnight. Remove chicken from marinade; scrape off and discard excess marinade.

2 Spray grill rack with nonstick spray. Preheat grill to medium or prepare medium fire.

3 Place chicken on grill rack and grill, turning occasionally, until chicken is cooked through, 30–35 minutes.

4 Transfer chicken to platter and spoon reserved lime mixture on top. Serve with lime wedges. Remove skin before eating.

SmartPoints value per serving (⅙ of chicken and 1 tablespoon lime mixture): 193 Cal, 6 g Total Fat, 1 g Sat Fat, 292 mg Sod, 6 g Total Carb, 4 g Sugar, 0 g Fib, 28 g Prot.

Let's do this together

For WW member Kam Szabo, this kind of recipe is a weeknight go-to. "Marinated grilled chicken, steamed broccoli, and a baked potato make an easy meal," she says. We agree!

Chicken and corn salad with yogurt-lime dressing

Gluten Free   **Serves 4**

Spiked with flavor from a creamy lime-coriander dressing, this is no ordinary chicken salad. Corn, cherry tomatoes, red onion, and cilantro lend color and texture to make this salad a summer standby.

¼   **cup plain low-fat yogurt**
¼   **teaspoon grated lime zest**
¼   **cup lime juice**
1   **tablespoon olive oil**
1   **teaspoon ground coriander**
¾   **teaspoon salt**
¼   **teaspoon chili powder**
Pinch cayenne
2   **large ears corn on the cob, shucked**
4   **(5-ounce) skinless boneless chicken breasts**
1   **cup cherry tomatoes, halved**
1   **small red onion, thinly sliced**
1   **cup fresh cilantro leaves**
1   **small head romaine lettuce, separated into leaves**

1 Spray grill rack with nonstick spray. Preheat grill to medium-high or prepare medium-hot fire.

2 To make dressing, whisk together yogurt, lime zest and juice, oil, coriander, ¼ teaspoon salt, the chili powder, and cayenne in large bowl. Let stand at room temperature.

3 Place corn on grill rack and grill, turning often, until corn is softened and browned, 15–17 minutes. Meanwhile, sprinkle chicken with remaining ½ teaspoon salt. Place chicken on grill rack and grill, turning often, until chicken is cooked through, 8–10 minutes.

4 Transfer chicken and corn to cutting board. When cool enough to handle, shred chicken and cut kernels from corn. Add chicken, corn, tomatoes, onion, and cilantro to dressing and toss to combine. Line 4 plates with romaine lettuce leaves; top evenly with chicken salad.

2 **SmartPoints value per serving** (1¾ cups salad and 2 lettuce leaves): 312 Cal, 9 g Total Fat, 2 g Sat Fat, 533 mg Sod, 24 g Total Carb, 8 g Sugar, 6 g Fib, 37 g Prot.

Chicken with tomato-zucchini salad

Gluten Free   Serves 4

This tomato and zucchini salad is delicious to make all summer long and goes with anything grilled. If you don't have grape tomatoes, use a large chopped tomato instead, and try basil, mint, or parsley instead of the cilantro.

2	**teaspoons grated lime zest**
3	**tablespoons lime juice**
2	**tablespoons white-wine vinegar**
1	**tablespoon olive oil**
3	**garlic cloves, minced**
4	**(5-ounce) skinless boneless chicken breasts**
1	**teaspoon ground cumin**
1¼	**teaspoons salt**
2	**cups grape or cherry tomatoes, halved**
1	**zucchini, diced (about 1½ cups)**
1	**jalapeño pepper, seeded and minced**
½	**small red onion, thinly sliced**
3	**tablespoons chopped fresh cilantro**

1 Combine lime zest and juice, vinegar, oil, and garlic in medium bowl. Transfer 3 tablespoons of mixture to zip-close plastic bag; add chicken and cumin. Squeeze out air and seal bag; turn to coat chicken. Refrigerate, turning bag occasionally, at least 1 hour or up to 4 hours. Reserve remaining marinade.

2 Spray grill rack with nonstick spray. Preheat grill to medium-high or prepare medium-high fire.

3 Remove chicken from marinade; discard marinade. Sprinkle chicken with 1 teaspoon salt. Place chicken on grill rack and grill, turning frequently, until chicken is cooked through, 8–10 minutes.

4 Meanwhile, to make salad, combine tomatoes, zucchini, jalapeño, onion, cilantro, remaining ¼ teaspoon salt, and reserved marinade in medium bowl and toss to coat. Serve chicken with salad.

1 **SmartPoints value per serving** (1 chicken breast and about ¾ cup salad): 235 Cal, 8 g Total Fat, 1 g Sat Fat, 799 mg Sod, 8 g Total Carb, 4 g Sugar, 2 g Fib, 33 g Prot.

Let's do this together

WW member Kathy Petrullo has a great tip for portioning skinless boneless chicken breasts. "I weigh and measure the portions before freezing them," she explains. "This saves time when I'm ready to cook and makes meal prep easier."

Chicken with tomato-zucchini salad

Chicken with couscous-mango salad

Serves 4

4	**(5-ounce) skinless boneless chicken breasts**
1	**cup mango nectar**
3	**garlic cloves, minced**
1½	**teaspoons grated lime zest**
2	**tablespoons plus ¼ cup lime juice**
1	**teaspoon ground cumin**
¾	**teaspoon salt**
½	**teaspoon black pepper**
1	**cup whole wheat couscous**
1	**tablespoon olive oil**
1	**teaspoon sugar**
½	**teaspoon minced chipotles en adobo**
¼	**cup chopped fresh cilantro**
2	**cups loosely packed baby arugula**
¼	**red onion, thinly sliced**
1	**mango, peeled, pitted, and cubed**

1 Place chicken, mango nectar, 2 garlic cloves, ½ teaspoon lime zest, 2 tablespoons lime juice, the cumin, ¼ teaspoon salt, and ¼ teaspoon pepper in large zip-close plastic bag. Squeeze out air and seal bag; turn to coat chicken. Refrigerate, turning bag occasionally, at least 1 hour or up to 4 hours.

2 Spray grill rack with nonstick spray. Preheat grill to medium-high or prepare medium-high fire.

3 Prepare couscous according to package directions. Transfer couscous to medium bowl and let cool to room temperature.

4 Remove chicken from marinade; discard marinade. Place chicken on grill rack and grill, turning often, until chicken is cooked through, 8–10 minutes.

5 Whisk together oil, sugar, chipotles, remaining 1 garlic clove, remaining 1 teaspoon grated lime zest, remaining ¼ cup lime juice, remaining ½ teaspoon salt, and remaining ¼ teaspoon pepper in large bowl. Stir in cilantro. Add couscous, arugula, onion, and mango and toss to coat. Serve chicken with salad.

 8

SmartPoints value per serving (1 chicken breast and 1¾ cups salad): 462 Cal, 8 g Total Fat, 1 g Sat Fat, 517 mg Sod, 60 g Total Carb, 24 g Sugar, 8 g Fib, 39 g Prot.

Let's do this together

For WW member Kathleen Messersmith, self-knowledge keeps her on track for healthy eating. "I know myself and if it's a late work night, I'm not going to prep veggies for dinner," she admits. "To set myself up for success, I make sure I have a dinner of leftovers or something that requires minimal work."

Chicken packets with zucchini and tomatoes

Gluten Free   Serves 4

4   **(5-ounce) skinless boneless chicken breasts**

¾   **teaspoon salt**

¼   **teaspoon black pepper**

2   **cups cubed zucchini**

4   **plum tomatoes, each cut into 6 wedges**

16   **Kalamata olives, pitted and sliced**

¼   **cup chopped fresh basil**

1 Preheat grill to medium-high or prepare medium-high fire. Tear off 4 (15 × 18-inch) sheets of heavy-duty foil.

2 Sprinkle chicken with ½ teaspoon salt and ⅛ teaspoon pepper. Place 1 chicken breast half on each sheet of foil.

3 Toss together zucchini, tomatoes, olives, remaining ¼ teaspoon salt, and remaining ⅛ teaspoon pepper in medium bowl. Arrange vegetable mixture evenly over chicken. Crimp foil into packets, making tight seal.

4 Place packets on grill rack and grill, covered, until chicken is cooked through and zucchini is tender, about 20 minutes. Let packets stand 5 minutes, then open with care to avoid steam. Transfer chicken and vegetables to plates, drizzle with juices, and sprinkle evenly with basil.

1 **SmartPoints value per serving** (1 chicken breast and ⅔ cup vegetables): 207 Cal, 6 g Total Fat, 1 g Sat Fat, 618 mg Sod, 5 g Total Carb, 3 g Sugar, 2 g Fib, 33 g Prot.

Cook's tip

Be sure to use heavy-duty foil for the grill packets, and seal them tightly to keep in all the steam and juices as your meal cooks.

**Chicken with
cucumber, orange,
and olive salad**

Chicken with cucumber, orange, and olive salad

Gluten Free   **Serves 4**

A quick marinade made with citrus juice and garlic adds some zing to ordinary chicken breasts. And the sweet and salty salad made with orange and olives is a colorful, crunchy, and flavorful accompaniment.

½   **cup fresh orange juice**

2   **tablespoons lime juice**

1   **tablespoon olive oil**

2   **garlic cloves, minced**

¾   **teaspoon salt**

¼   **teaspoon black pepper**

4   **(5-ounce) skinless boneless chicken breasts**

1   **cucumber, peeled, seeded, and diced**

1   **navel orange, peeled and diced**

1   **red bell pepper, diced**

¼   **cup lightly packed fresh cilantro leaves**

¼   **cup halved pitted Kalamata olives**

1 Spray grill rack with nonstick spray. Preheat grill to medium-high or prepare medium-high fire.

2 Whisk together orange juice, lime juice, oil, garlic, ¼ teaspoon salt, and the black pepper in small bowl. Transfer half of mixture to large zip-close plastic bag; add chicken. Squeeze out air and seal bag; turn to coat chicken. Refrigerate, turning bag occasionally, at least 1 hour or up to 4 hours. Reserve remaining orange juice mixture.

3 Meanwhile, stir together cucumber, orange, bell pepper, cilantro, olives, and remaining orange juice mixture in medium bowl. Set aside.

4 Remove chicken from marinade; discard marinade. Sprinkle chicken with remaining ½ teaspoon salt. Lightly spray chicken with olive oil nonstick spray. Place chicken on grill rack and grill, turning frequently, until chicken is cooked through, 8–10 minutes.

5 Place chicken on 4 plates and top evenly with salad.

 SmartPoints value per serving (1 chicken breast and ⅔ cup salad): 261 Cal, 9 g Total Fat, 1 g Sat Fat, 604 mg Sod, 12 g Total Carb, 7 g Sugar, 2 g Fib, 33 g Prot.

Freestyle it

While you grill the chicken, throw some zero Points veggies on the grill, too. Quick-cooking bell peppers, zucchini, yellow squash, asparagus, or eggplant will be ready in about the same time as the chicken.

Grilled chicken with tomato-anchovy sauce

Gluten Free   Serves 4

Anchovies add a savory, salty flavor to the marinade for the chicken in this recipe, as well as to the sauce served with it. Even if you don't like anchovies, we think you'll like this dish since they disappear into the sauce, leaving only their rich deep flavor.

1½ **cups lightly packed parsley leaves, plus ¼ cup chopped parsley**

6   **anchovy fillets, drained and patted dry with paper towels**

3   **tablespoons lime juice**

4   **teaspoons olive oil**

1   **tablespoon water**

1   **garlic clove, chopped**

¼   **teaspoon black pepper**

4   **(5-ounce) skinless boneless chicken breasts**

2   **plum tomatoes, chopped**

3   **tablespoons capers, drained**

1 Spray grill rack with nonstick spray. Preheat grill to medium-high or prepare medium-high fire.

2 Place 1½ cups parsley leaves, the anchovies, lime juice, oil, water, garlic, and pepper in mini–food processor and pulse until pureed. Transfer ¼ cup of mixture to shallow dish; add chicken and turn to coat. Let stand at room temperature 10 minutes.

3 To make sauce, place remaining parsley mixture in small bowl and stir in tomatoes, capers, and the remaining ¼ cup chopped parsley. Set aside.

4 Remove chicken from marinade; discard marinade. Place chicken on grill rack and grill, turning often, until chicken is cooked through, 8–10 minutes. Serve with sauce.

SmartPoints value per serving (1 chicken breast and about 2 tablespoons sauce): 239 Cal, 9 g Total Fat, 2 g Sat Fat, 450 mg Sod, 4 g Total Carb, 1 g Sugar, 1 g Fib, 34 g Prot.

Asian chicken with carrot-cucumber slaw

Serves 4

A bold soy, lime, and ginger combo serves as the flavorful marinade for this grilled chicken. With a tangle of colorful vegetable slaw on the side, this meal is healthy delicious cooking at is best.

4	**(5-ounce) skinless boneless chicken breast cutlets**
2	**tablespoons soy sauce**
2	**tablespoons lime juice**
1	**garlic clove, minced**
2	**teaspoons chopped peeled fresh ginger**
2	**teaspoons honey**
2	**teaspoons canola oil**
1½	**teaspoons Asian (dark) sesame oil**
¾	**teaspoon salt**
3	**radishes, cut into matchstick strips**
1	**small carrot, cut into matchstick strips**
½	**English (seedless) cucumber, cut into matchstick strips**
2	**tablespoons minced fresh cilantro**
1	**tablespoon minced fresh mint**

1 Combine chicken, soy sauce, 1 tablespoon lime juice, the garlic, ginger, 1 teaspoon honey, 1 teaspoon canola oil, and 1 teaspoon sesame oil in large zip-close plastic bag. Squeeze out air and seal bag; turn to coat chicken. Refrigerate, turning bag occasionally, at least 1 hour or up to 4 hours.

2 Spray grill rack with nonstick spray. Preheat grill to medium or prepare medium fire.

3 Whisk together remaining 1 tablespoon lime juice, remaining 1 teaspoon honey, remaining 1 teaspoon canola oil, remaining ½ teaspoon sesame oil, and ¼ teaspoon salt in small bowl and set aside. Combine radishes, carrot, cucumber, cilantro, and mint in large bowl and set aside.

4 Remove chicken from marinade; discard marinade. Sprinkle chicken with remaining ½ teaspoon salt. Place chicken on grill rack and grill, turning once, until chicken is cooked through, 6–8 minutes.

5 Add lime juice mixture to radish mixture and toss to coat. Serve chicken with salad.

 SmartPoints value per serving (1 chicken cutlet and about ½ cup salad): 203 Cal, 7 g Total Fat, 1 g Sat Fat, 959 mg Sod, 7 g Total Carb, 4 g Sugar, 1 g Fib, 27 g Prot

Cook's tip
Serve the chicken and slaw with warm rice noodles tossed with thinly sliced scallions and toasted sesame seeds (½ cup cooked rice noodles and 1 teaspoon sesame seeds will increase the per-serving SmartPoints value by 3).

Grilled chicken with shishito peppers

Serves 4

Grated zest and juice of
1 large lime

1½ **tablespoons soy sauce**

1 **tablespoon honey**

1 **shallot, minced**

2 **teaspoons canola oil**

4 **(5-ounce) skinless boneless chicken breasts**

1 **teaspoon Asian (dark) sesame oil**

¼ **pound shishito peppers**

¾ **teaspoon salt**

⅛ **teaspoon black pepper**

¼ **cup lightly packed fresh basil leaves, chopped**

¼ **cup lightly packed fresh cilantro leaves, chopped**

1 To make dressing, whisk together lime zest and juice, soy sauce, honey, shallot, and canola oil in small bowl.

2 Combine chicken, 3 tablespoons dressing, and the sesame oil in large zip-close plastic bag. Squeeze out air and seal bag; turn to coat chicken. Cover remaining dressing with plastic wrap. Refrigerate chicken and dressing at least 1 hour or up to 2 hours.

3 Spray ridged grill pan with nonstick spray and set over medium-high heat. Spray shishito peppers with nonstick spray and toss with ¼ teaspoon salt. Place shishito peppers on prepared pan and grill, turning once, until peppers are evenly charred, about 6 minutes. Transfer to platter.

4 Reduce heat to medium. Remove chicken from marinade; discard marinade. Sprinkle chicken with remaining ½ teaspoon salt and the black pepper. Place chicken on pan and grill, turning once, until chicken is cooked through, 8–10 minutes.

5 Arrange chicken on platter with shishito peppers. Drizzle with reserved dressing and sprinkle with basil and cilantro.

 SmartPoints value per serving (1 chicken breast, about ⅓ cup shishito peppers, and about 2½ teaspoons dressing): 241 Cal, 7 g Total Fat, 1 g Sat Fat, 829 mg Sod, 10 g Total Carb, 7 g Sugar, 1 g Fib, 33 g Prot.

Cook's tip

Shishito peppers are green finger-sized peppers that come with a gamble: About one in 10 will be spicy! They are thin-skinned and have tender seeds, so you can eat the whole pepper. If you can't find them, you can use mini bell peppers in this recipe.

**Grilled chicken with
shishito peppers**

**Chicken with
grapefruit-mint salsa**

Chicken with grapefruit-mint salsa

Gluten Free   Serves 4

This salsa, made with sweet-tart red grapefruit, spicy chile pepper, and fresh mint, can bring sunshine to a winter's day. If you're not a fan of grapefruit, make the salsa with 3 large navel oranges instead.

4   **(5-ounce) skinless boneless chicken breast cutlets**

½   **teaspoon ground cumin**

½   **teaspoon ground coriander**

½   **teaspoon plus pinch salt**

¼   **teaspoon black pepper**

2   **red or pink grapefruits, peeled, cut into segments, and diced**

¼   **cup sliced fresh mint**

1   **small shallot, diced**

½   **serrano pepper, seeded and minced**

1 Spray grill rack with nonstick spray. Preheat grill to medium or prepare medium fire.

2 Sprinkle chicken with cumin, coriander, ½ teaspoon salt, and the black pepper. Place chicken on grill rack and grill, turning once, until chicken is cooked through, 6–8 minutes.

3 Meanwhile, to make salsa, stir together grapefruit, mint, shallot, serrano pepper, and remaining pinch salt in medium bowl. Serve chicken with salsa.

0 **SmartPoints value per serving** (1 chicken cutlet and ¼ cup salsa): 217 Cal, 4 g Total Fat,1 g Sat Fat, 283 mg Sod, 12 g Total Carb, 10 g Sugar, 2 g Fib, 33 g Prot.

Cook's tip

To prepare the grapefruit, using a serrated knife, cut away the peel and white pith. Hold the fruit over a bowl and make cuts against the membrane on both sides of each section. Allow the sections to fall into the bowl. Squeeze the membrane to release the remaining juice. Remove any seeds.

Chicken with tomato, olive, and feta salad

Gluten Free   Serves 4

This simple grilled lemony chicken served with a salad made from foods you probably have in the fridge is an easy choice for a weeknight meal. Don't feel like grilling? Cook the chicken in your stovetop grill pan. Fresh out of mint? Use basil or parsley instead.

1   **pint grape tomatoes, halved**

¼   **cup pitted Kalamata olives, coarsely chopped**

¼   **cup crumbled reduced-fat feta**

2   **tablespoons thinly sliced fresh mint**

½   **tablespoon olive oil**

Grated zest and juice of 1 lemon

¼   **teaspoon black pepper**

½   **teaspoon salt**

4   **(5-ounce) skinless boneless chicken breast cutlets**

1 Spray grill rack with nonstick spray. Preheat grill to medium or prepare medium fire.

2 To make salad, combine tomatoes, olives, feta, mint, oil, lemon juice, and ⅛ teaspoon pepper in medium bowl; toss to mix well. Set aside.

3 Sprinkle chicken with lemon zest, salt, and remaining ⅛ teaspoon pepper. Place chicken on grill rack and grill, turning once, until chicken is cooked through, 6–8 minutes. Serve chicken with salad.

 **SmartPoints value per serving** (1 chicken cutlet and ½ cup salad): 226 Cal, 8 g Total Fat, 2 g Sat Fat, 512 mg Sod, 5 g Total Carb, 2 g Sugar, 1 g Fib, 34 g Prot.

Freestyle it
To make the salad more substantial, toss in some chopped romaine lettuce and thinly sliced water-packed roasted red peppers.

Vietnamese chicken thighs with mango relish

Serves 6

Be sure to trim any fat from the chicken thighs before adding them to the marinade. Not only does it save SmartPoints, it prevents flare-ups on the grill so your chicken will be succulent, not scorched!

Grated zest and juice of 1 orange

1   **jalapeño pepper, seeded and minced**

3   **garlic cloves, minced**

2   **tablespoons soy sauce**

1   **tablespoon Asian fish sauce**

1   **tablespoon packed brown sugar**

6   **(5-ounce) skinless boneless chicken thighs, trimmed**

1   **large mango, peeled, pitted, and diced**

⅓   **cup diced red onion**

¼   **cup chopped fresh mint**

3   **tablespoons unseasoned rice vinegar**

¼   **teaspoon salt**

Lime wedges

1 To make marinade, combine orange zest and juice, jalapeño, garlic, soy sauce, fish sauce, and brown sugar in large zip-close plastic bag; add chicken. Squeeze out air and seal bag; turn to coat chicken. Refrigerate, turning bag occasionally, at least 3 hours or up to overnight.

2 Spray grill rack with nonstick spray. Preheat grill to medium or prepare medium fire.

3 To make relish, stir together mango, onion, mint, and vinegar in serving bowl. Set aside.

4 Remove chicken from marinade; discard marinade. Sprinkle chicken with salt. Place chicken on grill rack and grill, turning often, until chicken is cooked through, about 15 minutes. Serve chicken with relish and lime wedges.

 3 **SmartPoints value per serving** (1 chicken thigh and about ¼ cup relish): 246 Cal, 6 g Total Fat, 2 g Sat Fat, 758 mg Sod, 18 g Total Carb, 14 g Sugar, 2 g Fib, 30 g Prot.

Let's do this together
For WW member Dr. Ronald E. Hunter, Jr., chicken thighs are a weeknight staple. He keeps a stash in the freezer along with a variety of frozen veggies. Rice is always on hand, too, and with the help of his rice cooker, it's a nearly effortless meal.

Chicken and veggie kebabs with romesco sauce

Gluten Free   Serves 4

2	**tablespoons sherry vinegar**
1½	**tablespoons extra-virgin olive oil**
½	**teaspoon smoked paprika**
¾	**teaspoon salt**
¼	**teaspoon black pepper**
1	**pound skinless boneless chicken breast, cut into 1½-inch pieces**
2	**red bell peppers**
1	**large ripe tomato, halved**
3	**tablespoons slivered almonds, toasted**
2	**garlic cloves, minced**
1	**zucchini, sliced ¾-inch thick**
8	**ounces cremini or button mushrooms, stems removed**

1 Combine 1 tablespoon vinegar, 1½ teaspoons oil, ¼ teaspoon paprika, ¼ teaspoon salt, and ⅛ teaspoon black pepper in large zip-close plastic bag; add chicken. Squeeze out air and seal bag; turn to coat chicken. Refrigerate, turning bag occasionally, at least 1 hour or up to 4 hours.

2 Spray grill rack with nonstick spray. Preheat grill to medium-high or prepare medium-high fire. Lightly spray peppers and tomato with olive oil nonstick spray. Place on grill rack and grill, turning often, until vegetables are charred, about 12 minutes for peppers and about 5 minutes for tomato. Place vegetables in small bowl; cover and let stand 10 minutes or until cool enough to handle. Peel peppers and tomato. Remove and discard seeds from peppers. Core tomato.

3 Combine bell peppers, tomato, almonds, garlic, remaining 1 tablespoon sherry vinegar, remaining 1 tablespoon oil, remaining ¼ teaspoon paprika, and ¼ teaspoon salt in blender or food processor. Pulse until mixture is smooth. Set aside. (The sauce may be made up to 2 days ahead and stored in covered container in refrigerator; bring to room temperature before serving.)

4 Remove chicken from marinade; discard marinade. Thread chicken, zucchini, and mushrooms onto 8 (10- to 12-inch) skewers. (If using wooden skewers, soak in water 20 minutes prior to use to prevent charring.) Lightly spray kebabs with olive oil nonstick spray. Place kebabs on grill rack and grill, turning occasionally, until chicken is cooked through, about 12 minutes. Sprinkle kebabs with remaining ¼ teaspoon salt and remaining ⅛ teaspoon black pepper. Serve kebabs with sauce.

(2) **SmartPoints value per serving** (2 kebabs and ¼ cup sauce): 258 Cal, 11 g Total Fat, 2 g Sat Fat, 497 mg Sod, 11 g Total Carb, 6 g Sugar, 4 g Fib, 30 g Prot.

Chicken and
veggie kebabs
with romesco
sauce

Chicken with orange and basil gremolata

Gluten Free   **Serves 6**

Infused with citrus, basil, and spices, this chicken is a flavorful addition to your warm-weather menus. If you don't want to fire up the grill, you can bake the chicken in a large shallow baking dish at 400°F for about 45 minutes.

1	large navel orange, zested in strips
1½	cups fresh orange juice
¼	cup lemon juice
½	cup thinly sliced fresh basil plus ¼ cup chopped fresh basil
2	small garlic cloves, finely minced
2	(3-inch) cinnamon sticks, broken in half
⅛	teaspoon cayenne
6	(5-ounce) skinless boneless chicken thighs, trimmed
½	teaspoon salt
1	teaspoon grated orange zest

1 Combine orange zest strips and juice, lemon juice, ½ cup sliced basil, 1 garlic clove, the cinnamon, and cayenne in large zip-close plastic bag; add chicken. Squeeze out air and seal bag; turn to coat chicken. Refrigerate, turning bag occasionally, at least 3 hours or up to overnight.

2 Meanwhile, spray grill rack with nonstick spray. Preheat grill to medium or prepare medium fire.

3 Remove chicken from marinade; discard marinade. Sprinkle chicken with salt. Place chicken on grill rack and grill, turning often, until chicken is cooked through, about 15 minutes.

4 To make gremolata, stir together remaining 1 garlic clove, remaining ¼ cup chopped basil, and the grated orange zest in small bowl. Transfer chicken to platter and sprinkle with gremolata.

(4) **SmartPoints value per serving** (1 chicken thigh): 207 Cal, 4 g Total Fat, 1 g Sat Fat, 195 mg Sod, 12 g Total Carb, 8 g Sugar, 1 g Fib, 29 g Prot.

Cook's tip
Using cinnamon sticks instead of ground cinnamon gives the chicken just a hint of spice. If you don't have a cinnamon stick, you can substitute ½ teaspoon ground cinnamon.

Moroccan-style chicken with olives

Gluten Free   Serves 4

The delectable rub for this chicken is a combination of Moroccan spices with olive oil and lemon. Serving it with grilled lemon wedges adds another hit of smoky flavor—and a beautiful garnish—to the plate.

2	**teaspoons grated lemon zest**
1	**teaspoon olive oil**
1	**teaspoon grated peeled fresh ginger**
1	**teaspoon fennel seeds, crushed**
¾	**teaspoon cinnamon**
¾	**teaspoon ground cumin**
¾	**teaspoon ground cardamom**
½	**teaspoon salt**
4	**(5-ounce) skinless boneless chicken thighs, trimmed**
2	**lemons, each cut into 4 wedges**
16	**pitted Kalamata olives, coarsely chopped**
¼	**cup chopped fresh flat-leaf parsley**

1 Combine lemon zest, oil, ginger, fennel seeds, cinnamon, cumin, cardamom, and salt in large zip-close plastic bag; add chicken. Squeeze out air and seal bag; turn to coat chicken. Refrigerate, turning bag occasionally, at least 1 hour or up to 4 hours.

2 Meanwhile, spray grill rack with nonstick spray. Preheat grill to medium-high or prepare a medium-high fire.

3 Remove chicken from bag. Place chicken on grill rack and grill, turning occasionally, until chicken is cooked through, about 15 minutes. Just before chicken is done, place lemon wedges on grill rack and grill, turning once, until lemons are lightly marked and slightly softened, 2–3 minutes. Transfer chicken and lemons to platter. Sprinkle chicken with olives and parsley.

5 **SmartPoints value per serving** (1 chicken thigh and 4 olives): 252 Cal, 12 g Total Fat, 3 g Sat Fat, 810 mg Sod, 7 g Total Carb, 1 g Sugar, 2 g Fib, 29 g Prot.

Freestyle it

For a 0 SmartPoints side dish, cut small zucchini lengthwise into spears, lightly spray with olive oil nonstick spray, and grill until crisp-tender, about 6 minutes. They'll taste great with the grilled lemons.

Grilled chicken with cucumber and herb salad

Grilled chicken with cucumber and herb salad

Gluten Free   Serves 4

Grated zest and juice of
1 lemon

3   teaspoons pomegranate
       molasses

2   teaspoons sumac

1   teaspoon chopped
       fresh thyme

4   (5-ounce) skinless boneless
       chicken thighs, trimmed

4   teaspoons olive oil

¾   teaspoon salt

¼   teaspoon black pepper

4   Persian cucumbers,
       sliced ½-inch thick

1½   cups fresh flat-leaf
       parsley leaves

1   cup fresh mint leaves

1   cup small cherry tomatoes,
       halved

½   small red onion,
       thinly sliced

1 Set aside 1 tablespoon lemon juice. Combine lemon zest, remaining lemon juice, 2 teaspoons pomegranate molasses, the sumac, and thyme in large zip-close plastic bag; add chicken. Squeeze out air and seal bag; turn to coat chicken. Refrigerate at least 1 hour or up to 4 hours.

2 Meanwhile, whisk together oil, reserved 1 tablespoon lemon juice, remaining 1 teaspoon molasses, ¼ teaspoon salt, and ⅛ teaspoon pepper in large bowl. Set aside.

3 Spray grill rack with nonstick spray. Preheat grill to medium or prepare medium fire.

4 Remove chicken from marinade; discard marinade. Sprinkle chicken with remaining ½ teaspoon salt and remaining ⅛ teaspoon pepper. Place chicken on grill rack and grill, turning once, until chicken is cooked through, 20–25 minutes. Cut chicken into thin slices.

5 Add cucumbers, parsley, mint, tomatoes, and onion to dressing; toss to coat. Divide salad evenly among 4 plates; top evenly with chicken.

(5) **SmartPoints value per serving** (1 chicken thigh and about 1¼ cups salad): 269 Cal, 11 g Total Fat, 2 g Sat Fat, 710 mg Sod, 13 g Total Carb, 5 g Sugar, 3 g Fib, 30 g Prot.

Let's do this together

Grilling chicken in batches is one of WW member Nancy Kunak's favorite ways to save time. She marinates chicken and grills it, then saves it for easy meals during the week. This recipe is perfect for trying her trick, so double up when you preparre the chicken for this salad for an effortless meal later on.

Soft turkey tacos with smoky tomatillo salsa

Gluten Free   Serves 4

Grilling the tomatillos for the sauce gives it a charred smoky flavor that's addictively delicious. Make a double batch and serve it over grilled or baked fish or shrimp for another meal.

6	tomatillos (about ¾ pound), papery husks removed, rinsed
¼	cup packed fresh cilantro leaves
2	tablespoons lime juice
2	teaspoons honey
1	chipotle en adobo
1	garlic clove, chopped
¾	teaspoon salt
4	(5-ounce) turkey cutlets
8	(6-inch) corn tortillas
1	cup mixed baby salad greens
4	radishes, thinly sliced

Lime wedges

1 Spray grill rack with nonstick spray. Preheat grill to medium-high or prepare a medium-high fire.

2 To make salsa, place tomatillos on grill rack and grill, turning often, until tomatillos are softened and lightly charred, 6–8 minutes. Transfer to food processor or blender. Add cilantro, lime juice, honey, chipotle, garlic, and ¼ teaspoon salt; pulse until almost smooth. Transfer salsa to small bowl; set aside.

3 Meanwhile, sprinkle turkey cutlets with remaining ½ teaspoon salt and lightly spray with olive oil nonstick spray. Place cutlets on grill rack and grill, turning once, until cutlets are well marked and cooked through, about 8 minutes. Transfer cutlets to cutting board. Let cool about 5 minutes, then thinly slice.

4 Place tortillas in single layer on grill rack and warm through, about 30 seconds on each side. Fill tortillas evenly with turkey, salad greens, radishes, and salsa. Serve with lime wedges.

(4) SmartPoints value per serving (2 tacos): 313 Cal, 5 g Total Fat, 1 g Sat Fat, 490 mg Sod, 32 g Total Carb, 6 g Sugar, 4 g Fib, 37 g Prot.

Freestyle it
Pile on the veggies to give these tacos more flavor, texture, and color. Chopped tomatoes, cilantro, jalapeños, or scallions would all be great add-ons.

Soft turkey tacos
with smoky
tomatillo salsa

Grilled turkey tacos with strawberry salsa

Gluten Free   **Serves 4**

When selecting strawberries for the salsa, choose berries with an intense aroma—those will be the freshest and ripest.

2   **teaspoons ground cumin**

1   **teaspoon ancho chile powder**

1¼ **teaspoons salt**

1¼ **pounds turkey cutlets**

½   **pound fresh strawberries, hulled and sliced**

1   **small ripe avocado, pitted, peeled, and diced**

1   **plum tomato, diced**

¼   **cup chopped fresh cilantro**

1   **shallot, thinly sliced**

3   **tablespoons lime juice**

2   **cups sliced romaine lettuce**

8   **(6-inch) corn tortillas, warmed**

Lime wedges

1 Stir together cumin, chile powder, and 1 teaspoon salt in small bowl. Rub turkey all over with spice mixture.

2 Spray ridged grill pan with nonstick spray and set over medium-high heat. Add turkey, spray with nonstick spray, and grill, turning once, until turkey is cooked through, 6–8 minutes.

3 Meanwhile, to make salsa, combine strawberries, avocado, tomato, cilantro, shallot, lime juice, and remaining ¼ teaspoon salt in medium bowl. Set aside.

4 Thinly slice turkey. Divide lettuce evenly among tortillas. Top evenly with turkey and salsa. Serve with lime wedges.

5 **SmartPoints value per serving** (2 tacos): 370 Cal, 10 g Total Fat, 1 g Sat Fat, 781 mg Sod, 36 g Total Carb, 5 g Sugar, 7 g Fib, 38 g Prot.

Let's do this together

WW member Kathleen Messersmith makes 0 SmartPoints fruit part of her daily habit. "I grab a banana as I leave the house every morning" she explains. "The school where I work makes fresh fruits available for students and staff for snacks, so I try to grab another one during the day as well."

Turkey cutlets with couscous-cucumber salad

Serves 4

Grated zest and juice of 1 orange

2 teaspoons minced fresh rosemary

1 garlic clove, minced

4 (¼-pound) turkey breast cutlets

1½ cups chicken broth

1 cup whole wheat couscous

¼ pound snow peas, trimmed and cut in half diagonally

¾ teaspoon salt

¼ plus ⅛ teaspoon black pepper

2 Persian cucumbers, quartered lengthwise and sliced

1 cup thinly sliced radishes

4 cups loosely packed baby spinach

1 Combine half of orange juice, the rosemary, and garlic in large shallow dish. Add turkey and turn to coat. Let stand while you prep couscous and snow peas.

2 Bring broth to boil in medium saucepan. Stir in couscous. Remove from heat, cover and let stand until broth is absorbed, about 5 minutes. Fluff with fork.

3 Meanwhile, bring medium saucepan of water to boil. Add snow peas and cook until bright green, about 5 seconds. Drain and rinse under cold running water until cool.

4 Spray ridged grill pan with nonstick spray and set over medium-high heat. Remove turkey from marinade and pat dry with paper towels. Sprinkle with ½ teaspoon salt and ¼ teaspoon pepper. Place in pan and cook, turning once, until well browned and cooked through, about 8 minutes. Transfer to plate.

5 Just before serving, stir together remaining half of orange juice, the orange zest, remaining ¼ teaspoon salt, and remaining ⅛ teaspoon pepper in large bowl. Add snow peas, cucumber, radishes, and couscous and toss gently to coat.

6 Divide spinach evenly among 4 plates and top evenly with salad. Place turkey on top of salad.

 **5** **SmartPoints value per serving** (1 turkey cutlet, 1 cup spinach, and 1½ cups salad): 350 Cal, 3 g Total Fat, 1 g Sat Fat, 887 mg Sod, 43 g Total Carb, 8 g Sugar, 8 g Fib, 37 g Prot.

Grilled turkey with watermelon and herb salad

Grilled turkey with watermelon and herb salad

Gluten Free   Serves 4

4	**(5-ounce) turkey cutlets**
2	**teaspoons grated lime zest**
5	**tablespoons lime juice**
1	**tablespoon olive oil**
½	**teaspoon ground cumin**
¾	**teaspoon salt**
¼	**teaspoon black pepper**
3	**cups ½-inch cubes seedless watermelon**
1	**cup loosely packed fresh mint leaves, torn**
1	**cup loosely packed fresh cilantro leaves**
½	**cup loosely packed fresh flat-leaf parsley leaves**
1	**shallot, thinly sliced**
¼	**cup crumbled feta**

1 Place turkey, 1 teaspoon lime zest, 2 tablespoons lime juice, ½ tablespoon oil, and the cumin in large zip-close plastic bag. Squeeze out air and seal bag; turn to coat turkey. Refrigerate, turning bag occasionally, at least 30 minutes or up to 1 hour.

2 Meanwhile, to make dressing, whisk together remaining 1 teaspoon lime zest, remaining 3 tablespoons lime juice, remaining ½ tablespoon oil, and ¼ teaspoon salt in large bowl. Set aside.

3 Spray grill rack with nonstick spray. Preheat grill to medium-high or prepare medium-high fire. Remove turkey from marinade; discard marinade. Sprinkle turkey with remaining ½ teaspoon salt and the pepper. Place turkey on grill rack and grill, turning once, until turkey is cooked through, 6–8 minutes.

4 Add watermelon, mint, cilantro, parsley, and shallot to dressing and toss to coat. Sprinkle salad with feta and serve with turkey.

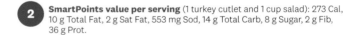

2 **SmartPoints value per serving** (1 turkey cutlet and 1 cup salad): 273 Cal, 10 g Total Fat, 2 g Sat Fat, 553 mg Sod, 14 g Total Carb, 8 g Sugar, 2 g Fib, 36 g Prot.

Cook's tip
For a change from feta, give ricotta salata a try. It's salted, pressed, and aged and has the same salty flavor as feta. Unlike feta, ricotta salata is not aged in brine, so it has a drier texture.

Grilled sausage and onion salad with figs

Gluten Free   Serves 4

1	medium sweet onion, cut into ½-inch-thick rings
3	(4-ounce) fully cooked chicken and apple sausage links
2	tablespoons extra-virgin olive oil
2	tablespoons pomegranate molasses
2	tablespoons lemon juice
¾	teaspoon salt, or to taste
½	teaspoon black pepper
4	cups baby spinach
1	head radicchio, trimmed and torn
½	cup fresh mint leaves, thinly sliced
8	fresh figs, halved
4	teaspoons pine nuts, toasted

1 Spray nonstick ridged grill pan with nonstick spray and set over medium-high heat. Lightly spray onion with nonstick spray. Add onion and sausages to pan and grill, turning onions once and sausages occasionally, until onions are tender and sausages are heated through, 6–8 minutes.

2 Meanwhile, to make dressing, whisk together oil, molasses, lemon juice, salt, and pepper in large bowl. Set aside.

3 Cut each sausage crosswise into 4 pieces. Add spinach, radicchio, and mint to dressing and toss to coat. Divide salad among 4 serving plates. Top evenly with sausage, onion, figs, and pine nuts.

 SmartPoints value per serving (3 pieces sausage, 2 figs, and about 2 cups onions and salad): 371 Cal, 17 g Total Fat, 3 g Sat Fat, 1,163 mg Sod, 42 g Total Carb, 30 g Sugar, 7 g Fib, 18 g Prot.

Let's do this together
WW member Sheri Friedman's key to success with the program is mapping all her meals for the week. "Knowing what the whole family is going to eat and having the foods I need on hand to stay on plan means the odds of having a good week skyrocket," she explains. "Failure to plan is planning to fail, right?"

Grilled sausage and onion
salad with figs

Chapter 3

Salads & sandwiches

Chicken niçoise salad with tarragon-olive vinaigrette, 78

Mustard-glazed chicken salad with mango and lime, 80

Rotisserie chicken: how to buy and use it at its best, 81

Chicken salad with farro and squash, 83

Chicken, spinach, and quinoa salad with olives, 84

Chicken panzanella with peppers and pine nuts, 85

Chicken and grape salad, 86

Succotash chicken salad with avocado dressing, 89

Asian peanut chicken salad, 90

Thai chicken salad, 92

Turkey fattoush salad, 93

Smoky turkey, quinoa, and roasted red pepper salad, 95

Turkey club salad with peppercorn dressing, 96

Turkey couscous salad with dried fruit and pine nuts, 98

Turkey sausage and roasted potato salad, 99

Chicken bahn mi sandwiches, 101

Open-face cobb salad sandwiches, 102

Thai ginger-chicken burgers, 103

Chicken sandwiches with pickled vegetable slaw, 104

Chutney chicken sliders, 107

Curried turkey and lentil burgers, 108

Chicken sausage and mushroom hoagies, 109

Open-face Greek turkey burgers, 111

Chicken niçoise salad with tarragon-olive vinaigrette

Gluten Free   Serves 4

Perfect for a summer picnic, this salad shows off potatoes, green beans, lettuces, and fresh tarragon at their peak. To pack it up for an al fresco lunch, store the dressing in a separate container and drizzle it on just before serving.

Salad

- ½ **pound fingerling potatoes**
- ½ **pound thin green beans, trimmed**
- 4 **(5-ounce) skinless boneless chicken breasts**
- ½ **teaspoon salt**
- ¼ **teaspoon black pepper**
- 1 **(5-ounce) package mixed baby salad greens**
- 4 **plum tomatoes, cut into wedges**
- 2 **hard-cooked eggs, quartered**
- 1 **small red onion, thinly sliced**

Paprika (optional)

Vinaigrette

- 2 **tablespoons white-wine vinegar**
- 1½ **tablespoons water**
- 1½ **tablespoons extra-virgin olive oil**
- ½ **teaspoon Dijon mustard**
- ⅛ **teaspoon black pepper**
- 8 **Kalamata olives, pitted and minced**
- 1 **small shallot, minced**
- 2 **teaspoons chopped fresh tarragon**

1 Bring large saucepan of salted water to boil. Add potatoes and cook until tender, about 8 minutes, adding green beans during last 2 minutes of cooking. Drain and rinse under cold running water until cool. Set aside.

2 Spray ridged grill pan with nonstick spray and set over medium-high heat until hot.

3 Sprinkle chicken with salt and pepper. Place chicken in grill pan and cook, turning occasionally, until chicken is cooked through, about 10 minutes. Transfer to cutting board and cut into slices.

4 Meanwhile, to make vinaigrette, whisk together vinegar, water, oil, mustard, and pepper in small bowl. Stir in olives, shallot, and tarragon. Set aside.

5 Cut potatoes in half lengthwise. Combine potatoes, beans, and 2 tablespoons vinaigrette in large bowl and toss to coat.

6 Divide greens evenly among 4 plates. Arrange potatoes, beans, tomatoes, eggs, and onion evenly on greens. Top evenly with chicken slices. Drizzle with remaining vinaigrette. Sprinkle with paprika, if using.

3 **SmartPoints value per serving** (about 3 cups salad, 1 chicken breast, and 2 tablespoons vinaigrette): 346 Cal, 13 g Total Fat, 2 g Sat Fat, 493 mg Sod, 20 g Total Carb, 4 g Sugar, 5 g Fib, 38 g Prot.

Chicken niçoise salad with tarragon-olive vinaigrette

Mustard-glazed chicken salad with mango and lime

Gluten Free **Serves 4**

This salad gets its kick from chicken coated with mustard, curry powder, and chutney. Served on a bed of romaine and radicchio, topped with mango, and drizzled with a lime-spiked yogurt dressing, this chicken is brimming with flavor.

1	**pound chicken breast tenders**
1	**tablespoon coarse-grained mustard**
2	**teaspoons curry powder**
2	**teaspoons mango chutney**
2	**teaspoons olive oil**
½	**teaspoon salt**
¼	**teaspoon black pepper**
1	**cup plain fat-free yogurt**
¾	**teaspoon grated lime zest**
2	**tablespoons lime juice**
2	**heads baby romaine (Little Gem) lettuce or 1 small head Bibb lettuce, leaves torn**
1	**small head radicchio, leaves torn**
1	**mango, peeled, pitted, and thinly sliced**

1 Preheat broiler. Line broiler rack with foil; spray foil with nonstick spray.

2 Arrange chicken on foil in single layer. Stir together mustard, curry powder, chutney, oil, ¼ teaspoon salt, and the pepper in small bowl. Brush mixture over chicken. Broil 5 inches from heat until chicken is cooked through, about 8 minutes (do not turn).

3 Meanwhile, to make dressing, stir together yogurt, ½ teaspoon lime zest, 1 tablespoon lime juice, and remaining ¼ teaspoon salt in small bowl. Set aside.

4 Arrange lettuce and radicchio in large shallow bowl. Add ½ cup dressing and toss to coat. Top with mango, drizzle with remaining 1 tablespoon lime juice, and sprinkle with remaining ¼ teaspoon lime zest. Top with chicken. Serve with remaining dressing.

1 **SmartPoints value per serving** (3 ounces chicken, about 2 cups salad, and ¼ cup dressing): 271 Cal, 6 g Total Fat, 1 g Sat Fat, 475 mg Sod, 23 g Total Carb, 19 g Sugar, 3 g Fib, 31 g Prot.

Cook's tip

Coarse-grained mustard is just that: mustard made with whole mustard seeds instead of ground mustard seeds. The whole seeds give the mustard a crunchy texture and intense flavor. If you have trouble finding it, try stone-ground mustard or, in a pinch, regular Dijon mustard.

Rotisserie chicken:
how to buy and use it at its best

Store-bought rotisserie chicken is the hero of shortcut dinners, whether you carve it up and enjoy it as is or incorporate its luscious meat in salads, sandwiches, pastas, and more. What makes it so good? The process of turning on a spit as they roast makes these birds wonderfully bronzed on all sides, and since juices are constantly recirculated during the roasting process, they're sublimely juicy at their best. Here's how to select and use a bird for a quick and delicious meal.

Look for plump

Choose the freshest, most succulent bird in the case, not one that's been sitting under heat lamps overcooking and losing moisture. The skin should be taut and shiny, not wrinkly. The bird should feel heavy when you lift it, with minimal juices leaked out in the container.

Ask for the freshest

If there's an attendant, ask which chickens are the most freshly roasted, or when new chickens will come out. You might assume the chickens are freshly roasted in the store, but if you don't see the rotisserie you should ask. Chickens cooked elsewhere and brought in may not have that just-roasted lusciousness we all crave.

Flavored or unflavored?

Plain salt-and-pepper birds are the norm, although you may see everything from Turkish spice to barbecue to Asian-flavored birds. Just be aware that these might be flavored with artificial ingredients and could also drastically increase the sodium content of your bird. If you're using the meat as an ingredient in a recipe—in tacos, for instance—you'll want to think about whether flavorings will clash with the other ingredients in your dish.

Store it properly

It's best and safest to head directly home with your chicken. If you won't be eating it immediately or using the meat in a recipe, you can transfer it to an oven-save dish, cover it with foil, and keep it in a 200-degree oven for up to an hour. Otherwise refrigerate it and reheat it.

Bird by the numbers

The best news: Minus the skin, rotisserie chicken breast is a zero Points food. That means you can use it in soups, salads, veggie bowls, sandwiches, tacos, and any number of other dishes without tracking. Enjoy! Here's a quick chart to help you calculate all parts of the chicken. (All values are for cooked skinless chicken.)

Piece of chicken	Weight	SmartPoints
Boneless breast	4 ounces	0
Boneless thigh	4 ounces	4
Drumstick (bone-in)	About 4 ounces	2

Chicken salad with
farro and squash

Chicken salad with farro and squash

Serves 4

½ cup farro

1 (20-ounce) package fresh peeled butternut squash, cut into ½-inch pieces

Grated zest of 1 orange (about ¾ teaspoon)

2 tablespoons orange juice

4 teaspoons extra-virgin olive oil

1½ teaspoons white balsamic vinegar

1 teaspoon grated peeled fresh ginger

½ teaspoon ground cumin

½ teaspoon salt

¼ teaspoon black pepper

2 cups diced cooked skinless boneless chicken breast

1 cup red seedless grapes, halved

⅓ cup fresh flat-leaf parsley leaves

3 tablespoons toasted pepitas (pumpkin seeds)

1 Preheat oven to 400°F. Spray large rimmed baking sheet with nonstick spray.

2 Bring farro and enough salted water to cover by 2 inches to boil in large saucepan. Reduce heat and simmer until farro is tender, about 40 minutes. Drain and cool.

3 Meanwhile, place squash on prepared baking sheet; spray lightly with olive oil nonstick spray and toss to coat. Spread squash in one layer and roast, stirring once halfway through baking time, until squash is tender, about 25 minutes. Let cool slightly.

4 To make dressing, whisk together orange zest and juice, oil, vinegar, ginger, cumin, salt, and pepper in large bowl.

5 Add farro, squash, chicken, grapes, and parsley to dressing; toss to coat. Serve sprinkled with pepitas.

5 **SmartPoints value per serving** (1½ cups): 348 Cal, 9 g Total Fat, 2 g Sat Fat, 359 mg Sod, 43 g Total Carb, 12 g Sugar, 12 g Fib, 27 g Prot.

Let's do this together

WW member swarner196 makes a big batch of 0 SmartPoints vegetable soup and adds different proteins, like leftover chicken or turkey, or leftover grains like farro or rice to make the soup taste different every day. "It makes for a very satisfying low- or 0 SmartPoints meal, and keeps me from getting bored ."

Chicken, spinach, and quinoa salad with olives

No Cook   **Gluten Free**   **Serves 4**

To turn this salad into a sandwich, serve it inside pita bread. A 2-ounce whole wheat pita bread will add 4 SmartPoints.

1	**(8-ounce) package frozen fully cooked quinoa (about 1¼ cups)**
4	**teaspoons extra-virgin olive oil**
1	**tablespoon white-wine vinegar**
1	**tablespoon water**
1	**teaspoon Dijon mustard**
½	**teaspoon smoked paprika**
½	**teaspoon salt**
¼	**teaspoon black pepper**
½	**shallot, minced**
3	**cups baby spinach**
1	**pint cherry tomatoes, halved**
2	**cups diced cooked skinless boneless chicken breast**
2	**thin celery stalks, thinly sliced**
12	**green olives, pitted and coarsely chopped**

1 Microwave quinoa according to package directions; drain well and cool.

2 Meanwhile, to make the dressing, whisk together oil, vinegar, water, mustard, paprika, salt, and pepper in large bowl. Whisk in shallot.

3 Add quinoa, spinach, tomatoes, chicken, celery, and olives to dressing; toss to coat.

 **4** **SmartPoints value per serving** (2 cups): 263 Cal, 10 g Total Fat, 2 g Sat Fat, 497 mg Sod, 18 g Total Carb, 3 g Sugar, 4 g Fib, 26 g Prot.

Let's do this together
Tracey Steckmeister, a WW member who's a pro at cooking healthy in a hurry, relies on precooked whole grains. "I've found that some specialty stores and large supermarkets sell cooked quinoa, farro, brown rice, and wild rice," she says. "They're a big help to cut down on prep time for meals."

Chicken panzanella with peppers and pine nuts

Serves 4

If you want to pump up the zero Points veggies, add some thinly sliced sweet onion to the mix when you roast the bell pepper mixture.

4	**ounces French baguette, cut into ½-inch cubes (about 2 cups)**
1	**large red bell pepper, thinly sliced**
1	**large orange or yellow bell pepper, thinly sliced**
12	**Kalamata olives, pitted and sliced**
3	**tablespoons pine nuts**
1	**teaspoon chopped fresh thyme**
4	**teaspoons extra-virgin olive oil**
1	**tablespoon balsamic vinegar**
1	**tablespoon water**
1	**teaspoon coarse-grained Dijon mustard**
½	**teaspoon salt**
¼	**teaspoon black pepper**
2	**cups cubed cooked skinless boneless chicken breast**
6	**cups baby arugula**

1 Preheat oven to 425°F. Line large rimmed baking sheet with nonstick foil.

2 To make croutons, spread bread cubes in even layer on prepared baking sheet. Spray with olive oil nonstick spray and toss to coat. Bake, stirring once, until croutons are golden, about 8 minutes. Transfer to plate.

3 Combine bell peppers, olives, pine nuts, and thyme on same baking sheet. Spray with olive oil nonstick spray, toss to coat, and spread in even layer. Bake until bell peppers are tender and nuts are toasted, about 12 minutes, stirring once halfway through baking time.

4 Meanwhile, to make dressing, whisk together oil, vinegar, water, mustard, salt, and black pepper in large bowl.

5 Add chicken, bell pepper mixture, croutons, and half of arugula to dressing; toss to coat. Add remaining arugula and toss again.

6 **SmartPoints value per serving** (2¼ cups): 318 Cal, 13 g Total Fat, 2 g Sat Fat, 632 mg Sod, 23 g Total Carb, 5 g Sugar, 3 g Fib, 27 g Prot.

Let's do this together

When WW member swarner196 gets home from her weekly shopping trip, she removes rotisserie chicken from the bone and shreds it so it's ready to use. "I use it in stir-fries, tacos, salads, pretty much anything," she says."Buying plain chicken already cooked makes it easy to season and customize for quick weeknight meals."

Chicken and grape salad

No Cook   Gluten Free   Serves 4

When fresh cherries are in season, you can make this salad using pitted and halved cherries.

¼   **cup reduced-fat mayonnaise**

2   **tablespoons plain low-fat Greek yogurt**

1   **teaspoon grated lemon zest**

3   **tablespoons lemon juice**

2   **tablespoons chopped fresh flat-leaf parsley**

2   **tablespoons minced red onion**

1   **teaspoon cumin seeds, crushed**

½   **teaspoon salt**

¼   **teaspoon black pepper**

2   **cups cubed cooked skinless chicken**

2   **thin celery stalks with leaves, thinly sliced**

2   **cups fresh grapes, halved**

6   **cups lightly packed spring greens salad mix**

1 Stir together mayonnaise, yogurt, lemon zest and juice, parsley, onion, cumin, salt, and pepper in large bowl. Stir in chicken, celery, and grapes.

2 Divide salad mix among 4 plates; top evenly with chicken mixture.

(4)   **SmartPoints value per serving** (1¼ cups chicken mixture and 1½ cups salad mix): 231 Cal, 8 g Total Fat, 2 g Sat Fat, 445 mg Sod, 16 g Total Carb, 11 g Sugar, 3 g Fib, 23 g Prot.

Let's do this together

WW member Brandy Evans finds that bringing her own lunch to work helps her remain in control of her eating plan. "Sometimes I make salads in a jar for the week ahead," she says. "When I take my lunch, it prevents me from overeating—which I do if I eat out—or from skipping lunch altogether."

Chicken and grape salad

Succotash chicken salad
with avocado dressing

Succotash chicken salad with avocado dressing

Gluten Free   Serves 4

The creamy, tangy dressing gets its thick consistency and rich flavor from pureed avocado. It elevates an ordinary salad to something special. You'll want to make it often for any type of salad or for serving as a dip.

1½ **cups frozen lima beans**

¾ **cup low-fat buttermilk**

½ **ripe avocado, pitted, peeled, and cut into cubes**

¼ **cup fresh flat-leaf parsley leaves**

1 **scallion, sliced**

1 **tablespoon lemon juice**

1 **small garlic clove, chopped**

½ **teaspoon salt**

¼ **teaspoon black pepper**

1 **large head Boston lettuce, separated into leaves**

2 **cups shredded cooked skinless chicken breast**

1½ **cups fresh corn kernels (from 3 ears)**

1½ **cups cherry tomatoes, halved**

1 **cucumber, peeled, halved lengthwise, seeded, and sliced**

2 **slices turkey bacon, cooked and sliced**

1 Cook lima beans according to package directions. Drain under cold running water until cool. Drain again and set aside.

2 Puree buttermilk, avocado, parsley, scallion, lemon juice, garlic, salt, and pepper in blender.

3 Place lettuce on large platter. Top with rows of chicken, lima beans, corn, tomatoes, cucumber, and bacon. Drizzle with dressing.

3 **SmartPoints value per serving** (generous 1½ cups salad, 1 cup lettuce, and ¼ cup dressing): 347 Cal, 8 g Total Fat, 2 g Sat Fat, 549 mg Sod, 40 g Total Carb, 8 g Sugar, 9 g Fib, 32 g Prot.

Asian peanut chicken salad

Serves 6

The peanut dressing for this salad makes a delicious dip for fresh veggies or a sauce for plain chicken breasts, too.

1   **cup frozen shelled edamame**
¼   **cup smooth peanut butter**
3   **tablespoons hoisin sauce**
3   **tablespoons rice vinegar**
2   **tablespoons water**
2   **teaspoons soy sauce**
¾   **teaspoon hot sauce**
1   **large scallion, sliced**
1   **teaspoon chopped peeled fresh ginger**
¾   **teaspoon salt**
6   **cups thinly sliced Napa cabbage**
2   **cups shredded cooked skinless boneless chicken breast**
2   **large carrots, shredded**
1   **English (seedless) cucumber, halved lengthwise and thinly sliced**
1   **cup lightly packed fresh cilantro leaves**

1   Bring small saucepan of water to boil over medium-high heat. Add edamame and cook 5 minutes. Drain, rinse under cold water, and pat dry. Transfer to large bowl.

2   Meanwhile, combine peanut butter, hoisin sauce, vinegar, water, soy sauce, hot sauce, scallion, ginger, and salt in blender and puree.

3   Add cabbage, chicken, carrots, cucumber, and cilantro to bowl with edamame. Add peanut butter mixture and toss to combine. Serve immediately.

3   **SmartPoints value per serving** (1½ cups): 236 Cal, 9 g Total Fat, 2 g Sat Fat, 613 mg Sod, 18 g Total Carb, 9 g Sugar, 4 g Fib, 21 g Prot.

Asian peanut chicken salad

Thai chicken salad

Gluten Free   Serves 6

This easy version of the Thai restaurant favorite larb adds rice noodles, which aren't traditionally used in the salad but make it a more filling meal. For an easy variation, you can serve it on top of shredded cabbage instead of inside the lettuce leaves.

2	**tablespoons canola oil**
3	**garlic cloves, minced**
2	**teaspoons minced peeled fresh ginger**
1	**pound ground skinless chicken breast**
6	**ounces thin rice noodles**
1	**red bell pepper, seeded and chopped**
1	**red onion, chopped**
1	**cucumber, peeled, seeded, and chopped**
1	**cup shredded carrots**
½	**cup chopped fresh mint**
⅓	**cup rice vinegar**
3	**tablespoons Asian fish sauce**
1	**tablespoon sugar**
1	**serrano pepper, seeded and chopped**
12	**Boston lettuce leaves**

1 Heat oil in large nonstick skillet over medium heat. Add garlic and 1 teaspoon ginger and cook until fragrant, about 30 seconds. Add chicken and cook, breaking it apart with wooden spoon, until chicken is lightly browned, 5–6 minutes. Remove from heat and let cool 5 minutes.

2 Meanwhile, place rice noodles in large bowl. Add enough boiling water to cover. Let stand until softened, about 5 minutes. Drain and coarsely chop noodles.

3 Combine bell pepper, onion, cucumber, carrots, mint, vinegar, fish sauce, sugar, serrano, and remaining 1 teaspoon ginger in large bowl. Add chicken and noodles; toss well.

4 Arrange 2 lettuce leaves on each of 6 plates. Fill each lettuce leaf with ½ cup chicken mixture. Serve at once.

5 **SmartPoints value per serving** (2 filled lettuce leaves): 281 Cal, 6 g Total Fat, 0 g Sat Fat, 784 mg Sod, 32 g Total Carb, 5 g Sugar, 2 g Fib, 21 g Prot.

Cook's tip
For more crunch and some nutty flavor, sprinkle each serving with 1 tablespoon dry roasted peanuts for an additional 2 SmartPoints.

Turkey fattoush salad

Serves 6

Fattoush is a Middle Eastern bread salad typically made with toasted flatbread. Our fresh and crunchy combo of pita bread, cucumbers, scallions, mint, and zero Points turkey breast makes a flavor-packed lunch or light summer dinner.

2	**(8-inch) whole wheat pitas**
6	**(4-ounce) turkey breast cutlets**
¾	**teaspoon salt**
¼	**teaspoon black pepper**
⅓	**cup fresh lemon juice**
⅓	**cup extra-virgin olive oil**
2	**small garlic cloves, crushed through a press**
2	**teaspoons ground sumac or ground coriander**
2	**teaspoons pomegranate molasses**
8	**small tomatoes, quartered**
4	**Persian cucumbers, halved lengthwise and sliced**
2	**scallions, thinly sliced**
1	**head romaine lettuce, chopped**
¼	**cup coarsely chopped fresh mint**

1 Preheat oven to 400°F. Line large baking sheet with foil.

2 Place pitas on prepared baking sheet; lightly spray both sides of pitas with olive oil nonstick spray. Bake until pitas are crisp, turning once, about 15 minutes. When cool enough to handle, break into bite-size pieces.

3 Meanwhile, spray ridged grill pan with nonstick spray; set over medium-high heat until hot. Sprinkle turkey with ¼ teaspoon salt, and the pepper. Add turkey to pan and cook, turning occasionally, until turkey is cooked through, about 6 minutes. Transfer to cutting board and let cool slightly.

4 Whisk together lemon juice, oil, garlic, sumac, molasses, and remaining ½ teaspoon salt in large bowl. Add tomatoes, cucumbers, scallions, lettuce, mint, and pita and toss well. Let stand until pita softens slightly, about 15 minutes.

5 Divide salad evenly among 6 plates. Cut turkey into thin slices and arrange over salads.

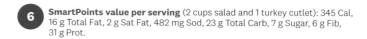

(6) **SmartPoints value per serving** (2 cups salad and 1 turkey cutlet): 345 Cal, 16 g Total Fat, 2 g Sat Fat, 482 mg Sod, 23 g Total Carb, 7 g Sugar, 6 g Fib, 31 g Prot.

Smoky turkey, quinoa, and roasted red pepper salad

Smoky turkey, quinoa, and roasted red pepper salad

Gluten Free   Serves 4

Smoked paprika, sweet roasted peppers, tart lemon, and crunchy pine nuts make this salad a riot of taste and texture. The turkey is served warm in the salad, making it an interesting contrast of temperature. Serve it on top of arugula for a bit more spicy flavor.

3   **(4-ounce) turkey breast cutlets**

2¼   **teaspoons smoked paprika**

½   **teaspoon salt**

4   **teaspoons olive oil**

1   **red onion, thinly sliced**

2   **garlic cloves, minced**

2   **tablespoons water**

1   **tablespoon lemon juice**

¼   **teaspoon black pepper**

1   **(4-ounce) package frozen cooked quinoa, thawed and squeezed dry, or 2½ cups cooked quinoa**

½   **cup water-packed roasted red peppers, drained and thinly sliced**

½   **cup chopped fresh parsley**

2   **tablespoons toasted pine nuts**

1 Sprinkle turkey with 2 teaspoons smoked paprika and ¼ teaspoon salt. Heat 2 teaspoons oil in large skillet over medium-high heat. Add turkey and cook, turning once, until turkey is browned and cooked through, about 8 minutes. Transfer turkey to cutting board.

2 Add onion to skillet and reduce heat to medium. Cook, stirring often, until onion is softened, about 3 minutes. Add garlic and cook, stirring constantly, until fragrant, 30 seconds. Add water and cook, stirring with wooden spoon to scrape up browned bits from bottom of pan, about 1 minute. Remove from heat.

3 Stir together lemon juice, black pepper, remaining 2 teaspoons oil, remaining ¼ teaspoon paprika, and remaining ¼ teaspoon salt in large bowl. Add quinoa, roasted peppers, parsley, pine nuts, and onion mixture. Cut turkey into thin slices and add to salad; toss to combine.

6   **SmartPoints value per serving** (about 1¼ cups): 335 Cal, 11 g Total Fat, 1 g Sat Fat, 393 mg Sod, 35 g Total Carb, 4 g Sugar, 5 g Fib, 27 g Prot.

Turkey club salad with peppercorn dressing

Serves 4

This recipe packs in all the flavors of your favorite sandwich, but as a salad instead. A light and creamy dressing, healthier turkey bacon, loads of greens, and skinny croutons make it a better-for-you choice for a hearty lunch.

6	slices turkey bacon, cut into ½-inch pieces
½	cup reduced-fat mayonnaise
¼	cup fat-free half-and-half
1	tablespoon lemon juice
1	teaspoon Dijon mustard
¼	teaspoon cracked black pepper
8	cups lightly packed salad greens
2	cups cubed cooked skinless turkey breast
10	cherry tomatoes, halved
1	cup plain fat-free croutons

1 Cook bacon in medium nonstick skillet over medium heat until crisp, about 3 minutes. Transfer to paper towels to drain.

2 To make dressing, whisk together mayonnaise, half-and-half, lemon juice, mustard, and pepper in serving bowl. Add salad greens, turkey, tomatoes, and croutons. Sprinkle with bacon; toss until coated evenly. Serve immediately.

 SmartPoints value per serving (2 cups): 350 Cal, 13 g Total Fat, 3 g Sat Fat, 827 mg Sod, 23 g Total Carb, 5 g Sugar, 5 g Fib, 33 g Prot.

Cook's tip
To give turkey bacon a little more flavor, sprinkle it with a pinch of black pepper or smoked paprika before cooking.

Turkey club salad with peppercorn dressing

Turkey couscous salad with dried fruit and pine nuts

Serves 8

When a honey-mustard dressing flavors a grain, fruit, and nut salad, what's not to love? The perfect combination of sweet, savory, salty, and crunchy, this easy salad will become a staple. Leftovers make a great lunch, too.

2	**cups chicken broth**
1	**cup couscous**
3	**tablespoons orange juice**
2	**tablespoons balsamic vinegar**
1	**tablespoon olive oil**
1	**teaspoon honey**
1	**teaspoon Dijon mustard**
½	**teaspoon salt**
¼	**teaspoon ground cumin**
½	**pound smoked turkey breast in one piece, cut into ½-inch cubes**
1	**cup red seedless grapes, halved**
1	**small red onion, diced**
⅓	**cup currants**
10	**pitted dates, chopped**
¼	**cup pine nuts, toasted**
3	**tablespoons chopped flat-leaf parsley**
8	**cups packed baby arugula or spinach**

1 Bring broth to boil in medium saucepan; stir in couscous. Cover and remove from heat; let stand 5 minutes. Gently fluff couscous with fork and transfer to large bowl. Let cool slightly.

2 Meanwhile, whisk together orange juice, vinegar, oil, honey, mustard, salt, and cumin in small bowl. Stir orange juice mixture into couscous.

3 Add turkey, grapes, onion, currants, dates, pine nuts, and parsley to couscous mixture; toss well to combine. Divide arugula evenly among 8 plates; top evenly with salad. Serve warm or at room temperature.

(6) **SmartPoints value per serving** (about ¾ cup salad and 1 cup arugula): 227 Cal, 5 g Total Fat, 1 g Sat Fat, 501 mg Sod, 35 g Total Carb, 14 g Sugar, 3 g Fib, 11 g Prot.

Cook's tip
Substitute your favorite dried fruits instead of the currants and dates called for in this recipe. Dried cranberries or cherries, raisins, or chopped dried apricots or figs work well.

Turkey sausage and roasted potato salad

Gluten Free   **Serves 6**

This salad takes hearty sausages and potatoes and turns them into a healthy main-dish salad that's loaded with veggies. Baby kale adds a touch of bitterness and crunch, while roasted red peppers balance the dish with sweetness.

1¼	**pounds red potatoes, scrubbed and cut into 1-inch chunks**
1	**teaspoon dried thyme**
¾	**teaspoon salt**
¾	**teaspoon black pepper**
1	**pound fresh sweet Italian turkey sausages**
1	**(7-ounce) jar water-packed roasted red peppers, drained and chopped**
½	**cup thinly sliced red onion**
¼	**cup black olives, pitted and chopped**
3	**tablespoons red-wine vinegar**
2	**tablespoons country-style Dijon mustard**
1	**tablespoon extra-virgin olive oil**
6	**cups baby kale**

1 Preheat oven to 425°F. Spray medium roasting pan with nonstick spray.

2 Combine potatoes, thyme, ½ teaspoon salt, and ½ teaspoon black pepper in large bowl. Lightly spray potatoes with olive oil nonstick spray; toss to coat. Arrange potatoes in prepared pan in single layer. Roast, stirring occasionally, until potatoes are tender and browned, about 40 minutes. Transfer potatoes to large bowl; set aside.

3 Spray broiler rack with nonstick spray; preheat broiler. Arrange sausage on rack. Broil 7 inches from heat, turning occasionally, until sausage is browned and cooked through, about 15 minutes. Let sausage cool slightly. Cut diagonally into 1-inch chunks; add to potatoes. Stir in roasted peppers, onion, and olives.

4 Whisk together vinegar, mustard, oil, remaining ¼ teaspoon salt, and remaining ¼ teaspoon black pepper in small bowl.

5 Place kale in large bowl; drizzle with 1 tablespoon dressing and toss to coat. Place on large platter. Add remaining dressing to sausage mixture and toss to coat. Place sausage mixture on top of kale and serve at once.

6 **SmartPoints value per serving** (1½ cups sausage mixture and 1 cup kale): 236 Cal, 10 g Total Fat, 2 g Sat Fat, 1,018 mg Sod, 23 g Total Carb, 3 g Sugar, 3 g Fib, 14 g Prot.

Cook's tip
Use tongs to turn the sausage when broiling. Piercing the sausage with a fork will cause the juices to escape.

**Chicken bahn mi
sandwiches**

Chicken bahn mi sandwiches

Serves 4

If you have time, double up on the pickled vegetables in this recipe. They add great flavor and crunch to any sandwich, or enjoy them with a meal as a fresh and crunchy side dish.

2	**tablespoons soy sauce**
1	**tablespoon lime juice**
2	**garlic cloves, minced**
1	**pound skinless boneless chicken breast cutlets**
¼	**cup unseasoned rice vinegar**
1	**teaspoon sugar**
⅛	**teaspoon salt**
½	**cup thinly sliced sweet onion**
1	**small carrot, coarsely shredded**
¼	**cup reduced-fat mayonnaise**
2	**teaspoons Sriracha**
4	**(3-ounce) sandwich rolls, split**
½	**English (seedless) cucumber, thinly sliced**
¼	**cup fresh cilantro leaves**

1 Combine soy sauce, lime juice, and garlic in large zip-close plastic bag; add chicken. Squeeze out air and seal bag; turn to coat chicken. Refrigerate at least 30 minutes or up to 4 hours.

2 Meanwhile, to make pickled vegetables, stir together vinegar, sugar, and salt in small bowl. Add onion and carrot and stir to coat. Cover and refrigerate at least 30 minutes or up to 1 day.

3 Spray large ridged grill pan with nonstick spray and set over medium-high heat. Remove chicken from marinade; discard marinade. Add chicken to pan and cook, turning once, until chicken is cooked through, 6–8 minutes. Thinly slice chicken.

4 Stir together mayonnaise and Sriracha in small bowl. Remove soft centers from rolls and discard, or save for bread crumbs. Spread 1 tablespoon mayonnaise mixture on cut side of each roll.

5 Drain pickled vegetables. Fill rolls evenly with chicken, cucumber, pickled vegetables, and cilantro. (Alternatively, use a 12-ounce roll and cut sandwich into 4 equal portions.)

6   **SmartPoints value per serving** (1 sandwich): 354 Cal, 8 g Total Fat, 1 g Sat Fat, 1,026 mg Sod, 36 g Total Carb, 6 g Sugar, 2 g Fib, 31 g Prot.

Let's do this together

Here's a time-saving tip for from WW member Dr. Ronald E. Hunter Jr. He puts his chicken breasts in a marinade in a zip-close bag and then freezes them. When they defrost overnight in the refrigerator, the marinade soaks into the chicken for a ready-to-cook dinner that's infused with flavor.

Open-face cobb salad sandwiches

Serves 4

Buttermilk lends creaminess and tang to this salad dressing. If it's not something you keep on hand, try the same amount of plain fat-free yogurt instead.

2	**(5-ounce) skinless boneless chicken breasts**
¾	**teaspoon herbes de Provence or dried thyme**
¾	**teaspoon salt**
½	**teaspoon black pepper**
⅓	**cup fat-free buttermilk**
1	**tablespoon reduced-fat mayonnaise**
1	**scallion, finely chopped**
1	**teaspoon red-wine vinegar**
4	**slices country-style whole-grain bread, toasted**
2	**cups lightly packed trimmed watercress**
½	**Hass avocado, pitted, peeled, and thinly sliced**
1	**tomato, sliced**
1	**hard-cooked large egg, peeled and sliced**
¼	**cup crumbled reduced-fat blue cheese**
2	**slices turkey bacon, cooked crisp and crumbled**

1 Spray ridged grill pan with nonstick spray and set over medium-high heat.

2 Sprinkle chicken with herbes de Provence, ½ teaspoon salt, and ¼ teaspoon pepper. Place chicken in grill pan and cook, turning once, until chicken is lightly browned and cooked through, about 8 minutes. Transfer chicken to cutting board.

3 Meanwhile, to make dressing, whisk together buttermilk, mayonnaise, scallion, vinegar, remaining ¼ teaspoon salt, and remaining ¼ teaspoon pepper in small bowl.

4 Thinly slice chicken on diagonal. Top each slice of bread with one-quarter each of watercress, chicken, avocado, tomato, and egg. Spoon one-quarter of dressing over each sandwich; sprinkle evenly with blue cheese and bacon.

5 **SmartPoints value per serving** (1 sandwich): 273 Cal, 10 g Total Fat, 3 g Sat Fat, 881 mg Sod, 20 g Total Carb, 4 g Sugar, 3 g Fib, 24 g Prot.

Let's do this together

Not sure what to do with the other half of the avocado leftover from this recipe? Take a delicious tip from WW member Nancy Kunak and toss cubed avocado and tomato with diced red onion, a drizzle of olive oil, and salt and pepper for an easy, colorful side salad.

Thai ginger-chicken burgers

Serves 4

If you have trouble finding ground skinless chicken breast, you can substitute ground skinless turkey breast, which is more commonly available.

1   **pound ground skinless chicken breast**

2   **scallions, white and light green parts only, finely chopped**

⅓   **cup chopped fresh cilantro**

1   **tablespoon minced peeled fresh ginger**

Grated zest of 1 lime

½   **teaspoon salt**

¼   **teaspoon black pepper**

2   **teaspoons canola oil**

¼   **cup reduced-fat mayonnaise**

1½   **teaspoons Sriracha**

4   **light hamburger buns, toasted**

16   **thin slices English (seedless) cucumber**

4   **thin slices red onion**

Lime wedges

1   Combine chicken, scallions, cilantro, ginger, ½ teaspoon lime zest, the salt, and pepper in large bowl. Using damp hands, form mixture into 4 (¾-inch-thick) patties.

2   Heat oil in large nonstick skillet over medium heat. Add patties and cook, turning once, until instant-read thermometer inserted into side of burger registers 165°F, about 8 minutes.

3   Meanwhile, combine mayonnaise, Sriracha, and remaining lime zest in small bowl. Spread cut sides of buns with mayonnaise mixture.

4   Serve burgers in buns topped with cucumber and onion. Serve with lime wedges.

(5)   **SmartPoints value per serving** (1 garnished burger): 293 Cal, 9 g Total Fat, 1 g Sat Fat, 691 mg Sod, 22 g Total Carb, 4 g Sugar, 4 g Fib, 29 g Prot.

Let's do this together

WW member Kelly H. packs her own snacks. "No matter how busy I am, it honestly doesn't take long to cut up some cucumbers and carrots and throw them in a small soft-sided cooler. And I almost always have an apple and a pack of almonds in my purse."

Chicken sandwiches with pickled vegetable slaw

Serves 4

Marinating the chicken makes it moist and full of flavor, and the vegetable slaw adds crunch and tang. If you're short on time, skip the slaw and top the sandwiches with lettuce or arugula and tomato or cucumber slices and they'll still be delicious.

⅔   **cup low-fat buttermilk**

2   **garlic cloves, crushed through a press**

¼   **teaspoon cayenne**

4   **(5-ounce) skinless boneless chicken breast cutlets**

6   **tablespoons unseasoned rice vinegar**

2   **tablespoons water**

½   **red bell pepper, very thinly sliced**

½   **yellow bell pepper, very thinly sliced**

1   **carrot, cut into thin matchstick strips**

¼   **red onion, very thinly sliced**

½   **teaspoon plus ⅛ teaspoon salt**

2   **tablespoons chopped fresh flat-leaf parsley**

4   **teaspoons honey mustard**

4   **ciabatta rolls, split and soft centers removed**

1 To make marinade, combine buttermilk, garlic, and cayenne in large zip-close plastic bag; add chicken. Squeeze out air and seal bag; turn to coat chicken. Refrigerate at least 1 hour or up to 2 hours.

2 To make pickled vegetables, combine vinegar, water, bell peppers, carrot, and onion in large zip-close plastic bag. Squeeze out air and seal bag; turn to mix well. Refrigerate at least 1 hour or up to 2 hours.

3 Spray ridged grill pan with nonstick spray; set over medium-high heat until hot. Remove chicken from marinade; discard marinade. Sprinkle chicken with ½ teaspoon salt. Place chicken in pan and cook, turning once, until chicken is browned and cooked through, 6–8 minutes.

4 Drain vegetable mixture and transfer to medium bowl. Add parsley and remaining ⅛ teaspoon salt; toss to mix well. Spread mustard on bottoms of rolls. Top each with 1 cutlet and one-quarter pickled vegetables; cover with tops of rolls.

 SmartPoints value per serving (1 sandwich): 397 Cal, 7 g Total Fat, 2 g Sat Fat, 831 mg Sod, 41 g Total Carb, 8 g Sugar, 3 g Fib, 40 g Prot.

**Chicken sandwiches
with pickled
vegetable slaw**

Chutney chicken sliders

Chutney chicken sliders

Serves 6

To add more spice and crunch to the sliders, top them with peppery baby arugula and crispy cucumber slices.

¾ cup mango chutney, large pieces chopped

2 scallions, thinly sliced

2 teaspoons hot sauce

2 teaspoons curry powder

¾ teaspoon salt

⅓ cup panko (bread crumbs)

1¼ pounds ground skinless chicken breast or ground skinless turkey breast

2 teaspoons canola oil

12 small (1-ounce) whole-grain dinner rolls, split

Bibb lettuce leaves

1 Combine ⅓ cup of chutney, the scallions, hot sauce, curry powder, and salt in medium bowl. Stir in panko. Add chicken and stir just until combined. Do not overmix.

2 Heat 1 teaspoon oil in large nonstick skillet over medium heat. Drop half of chicken mixture by ¼-cup measures into skillet, about 2 inches apart. Press down with spatula to form six 2½-inch-diameter patties.

3 Cook, turning once, until patties are cooked through, about 8 minutes. Repeat with remaining 1 teaspoon oil and remaining chicken mixture.

4 Serve patties in rolls topped with remaining chutney and lettuce leaves.

10 **SmartPoints value per serving** (2 sliders): 381 Cal, 8 g Total Fat, 1 g Sat Fat, 829 mg Sod, 47 g Total Carb, 14 g Sugar, 3 g Fib, 27 g Prot.

Let's do this together

WW member Lindsay Smith pumps up the veggies in her family's meals by roasting or grilling their favorites. "We love them," says this busy mother of two young girls. "Kale, cabbage, carrots, zucchini, eggplant, Brussels sprouts, broccoli, and cauliflower are all delicious options for us."

Curried turkey and lentil burgers

Serves 4

Depending on the brand you buy, chutney can be chunky. If yours has very large pieces of fruit, put the amount you need for the recipe in a small bowl and use kitchen scissors to snip it into smaller pieces.

- ¾ **pound ground skinless turkey breast**
- ½ **cup canned lentils, rinsed and drained**
- ⅓ **cup shredded carrot**
- 1 **roasted red pepper (water-packed), drained and minced**
- 2 **tablespoons chopped fresh cilantro**
- 1 **tablespoon minced shallot**
- 2½ **teaspoons curry powder**
- ½ **teaspoon salt**
- 2 **teaspoons canola oil**
- 2 **tablespoons mango or other fruit chutney**
- 2 **tablespoons reduced-fat mayonnaise**
- 4 **sandwich thins, toasted**
- 4 **Bibb lettuce leaves**
- 4 **slices tomato**
- 1 **cup English (seedless) cucumber slices**

1 Combine turkey, lentils, carrot, roasted pepper, cilantro, shallot, curry powder, and salt in large bowl; mix well. Form mixture into 4 (½-inch-thick) patties.

2 Heat oil in large nonstick skillet over medium heat. Add burgers and cook, turning once, until instant-read thermometer inserted into side of burger registers 165°F, about 10 minutes.

3 Meanwhile, stir together chutney and mayonnaise in small bowl.

4 Serve burgers in sandwich thins, topped with chutney mixture, lettuce, tomato, and cucumber.

5 **SmartPoints value per serving** (1 burger): 281 Cal, 7 g Total Fat, 1 g Sat Fat, 625 mg Sod, 30 g Total Carb, 7 g Sugar, 4 g Fib, 26 g Prot.

Let's do this together

WW member Amanda Sanchez says she can't live without her food scale and measuring cups and spoons. "Healthy food or not, the amount you eat matters and in America, our perception of serving size is distorted," she says. "I've learned to weigh or measure everything!"

Chicken sausage and mushroom hoagies

Serves 4

Hoisin sauce sounds like an odd ingredient for a hoagie, but it lends just the right amount of sweetness to the spicy sausages and savory mushrooms. If you're doubtful, have it with mustard, instead!

1	teaspoon olive oil
3	fully cooked hot Italian chicken sausages, sliced (8 ounces)
1	red onion, halved and thinly sliced
½	pound cremini mushrooms, sliced
2	garlic cloves, minced
	Salt to taste
4	(6-inch) whole wheat hoagie rolls (3 ounces each), split
¼	cup hoisin sauce
½	cup shredded part-skim mozzarella
¼	cup chopped fresh cilantro
1	scallion, thinly sliced

1 Heat oil in large nonstick skillet over medium heat. Add sausage and cook, stirring often, until sausage is lightly browned, 3–4 minutes. Transfer sausage to plate. Add onion to skillet and cook, stirring occasionally, until onion is softened, about 5 minutes. Stir in mushrooms and garlic. Cook, stirring occasionally, until mushrooms are tender, about 8 minutes. Season to taste with salt.

2 Preheat broiler. Pull out some of soft centers from rolls. Place rolls cut sides up on broiler pan. Broil 5 inches from heat until toasted, about 1 minute.

3 Spread hoisin sauce on cut sides of rolls. Top bottom halves of rolls with mushroom mixture. Arrange sausage on top halves of rolls. Sprinkle mozzarella evenly over rolls. Broil 5 inches from heat until cheese melts, about 1 minute. Sprinkle with cilantro and scallion, then put halves together to make sanwhiches.

12 **SmartPoints value per serving** (1 sandwich): 406 Cal, 12 g Total Fat, 3 g Sat Fat, 1,159 mg Sod, 56 g Total Carb, 15 g Sugar, 8 g Fib, 22 g Prot.

Cook's tip
Cremini mushrooms are baby portabello mushrooms. They're the same size and shape as ordinary white mushrooms, but they're a dark brown color and have a meatier, more intense flavor.

Open-face Greek turkey burgers

Open-face Greek turkey burgers

Serves 4

Bulgur wheat is the main ingredient in tabbouleh salad, and it makes a healthy, high-fiber addition to salads, soups, burgers, and meat loaves.

1	cup water
½	cup bulgur wheat
1	teaspoon salt
½	cup plain low-fat Greek yogurt
1½	tablespoons chopped fresh mint
1	garlic clove, minced
¾	pound ground skinless turkey breast
¼	cup finely chopped red onion
¼	cup chopped fresh parsley
1	egg white
½	teaspoon cinnamon
½	teaspoon ground allspice
¼	teaspoon black pepper
2	teaspoons olive oil
4	(4-inch) mini–pita breads, warmed
4	Bibb lettuce leaves
4	tomato slices
16	thin slices English (seedless) cucumber

1 Bring water to boil in small saucepan. Add bulgur and ⅛ teaspoon salt. Cover, reduce heat, and simmer until water is almost absorbed, about 10 minutes. Remove from heat and let stand 5 minutes. Fluff with fork and transfer to medium shallow dish to cool slightly.

2 Meanwhile, stir together yogurt, mint, garlic, and ⅛ teaspoon salt in small bowl. Set aside.

3 To make burgers, stir together turkey, bulgur, onion, parsley, egg white, cinnamon, allspice, pepper, and remaining ¾ teaspoon salt in large bowl. With damp hands, shape mixture into 4 patties.

4 Heat oil in large nonstick skillet over medium heat. Add burgers and cook, turning once, until instant-read thermometer inserted into side of burger registers 165°F, 10–12 minutes.

5 Place pitas on 4 plates. Top with burgers, lettuce leaves, tomato slices, and cucumber slices. Spoon yogurt mixture evenly on top of burgers.

5   **SmartPoints value per serving** (1 burger and 2 tablespoons sauce): 295 Cal, 5 g Total Fat, 1 g Sat Fat, 737 mg Sod, 34 g Total Carb, 3 g Sugar, 4 g Fib, 30 g Prot.

Let's do this together

WW member Kathy Petrullo loves the rich, creamy taste of plain low-fat Greek yogurt and finds many uses for it in her cooking. "I use it to top steel-cut oats and baked potatoes, I stir in herbs and use it as a salad dressing or dip, and it makes a delicious parfait in a fancy glass with fruits," she says.

Chapter 4

One-pan dinners

Tomato-stuffed chicken with roasted fennel, 114

Rosemary-garlic baked chicken, 116

Sheet-pan cheat sheet, 117

Rosemary-prosciutto chicken with potatoes, 119

Roasted Greek-style chicken and vegetables, 120

Chicken vegetable udon soup, 121

Chicken with fresh tomato sauce, 122

Chicken and eggplant stir-fry with snow peas, 125

Chicken vegetable noodle bowl, 126

Lemon-rosemary chicken with radicchio, 128

Slow cooker balsamic-braised chicken with kale, 129

Slow cooker chicken stew with roasted-pepper rouille, 130

Braised chicken with potatoes and artichokes, 131

Lemon chicken with white beans and stuffed peppers, 133

Roast chermoula chicken with butternut squash, 134

Turkey, red bean, and chipotle pepper chili, 135

Tandoori chicken skewers with roasted vegetables, 136

Lentil and chorizo soup with kale, 139

Thai turkey and broccoli stir-fry, 140

Turkey-tomatillo chili, 143

Southwest turkey and vegetable soup, 144

Tuscan sausage and bean stew, 145

Tomato-stuffed chicken with roasted fennel

Gluten Free   Serves 4

In this flavorful dish, succulent chicken breasts are filled with fresh tomatoes and sharp Romano and served with fennel that's roasted with bacon. It's a meal that's impressive enough for company and takes only about 45 minutes to make.

4	plum tomatoes
4	(5-ounce) skinless boneless chicken breasts
1	teaspoon salt
½	teaspoon black pepper
¼	cup grated Romano
1	teaspoon minced fresh thyme, plus 4 fresh thyme sprigs
2	teaspoons fennel seeds, crushed
2	small fennel bulbs, each cut into 8 wedges, fronds reserved
2	slices center-cut bacon, chopped
3	tablespoons dry white wine
1	tablespoon olive oil
1	tablespoon lemon juice

1 Preheat oven to 425°F. Spray large rimmed sheet pan with nonstick spray.

2 Cut 2 tomatoes into 6 slices each. Halve the remaining 2 tomatoes lengthwise. Set aside.

3 Place chicken on cutting board. Holding sharp knife parallel to board and starting at one side, cut three-quarters of way through chicken and open up like a book. Sprinkle chicken with ½ teaspoon salt and ⅛ teaspoon pepper. Place 2 tomato slices on bottom half of each chicken breast. Sprinkle tomatoes evenly with Romano and minced thyme. Close top of each chicken breast over tomatoes. Place chicken in center of prepared pan. Top chicken with remaining 4 tomato slices; sprinkle with fennel seeds, ¼ teaspoon salt, and ⅛ teaspoon pepper. Top tomato slices with thyme sprigs.

4 Arrange fennel wedges in single layer in pan; sprinkle fennel with bacon. Arrange tomato halves in single layer in pan. Drizzle chicken, fennel, and tomatoes with wine, oil, and lemon juice; sprinkle tomatoes and fennel with remaining ¼ teaspoon salt and remaining ¼ teaspoon pepper.

5 Roast chicken and vegetables, without turning, until chicken is cooked through, tomatoes begin to shrivel, and fennel is crisp-tender, 25–30 minutes.

6 Transfer to plates; spoon any cooking juices over chicken. Sprinkle with chopped fennel fronds.

(2) **SmartPoints value per serving** (1 stuffed chicken breast, 4 fennel wedges, and ½ tomato): 283 Cal, 10 g Total Fat, 2 g Sat Fat, 846 mg Sod, 10 g Total Carb, 0 g Sugar, 4 g Fib, 35 g Prot.

Tomato-stuffed chicken with roasted fennel

Rosemary-garlic baked chicken

Gluten Free **Serves 6**

Ordinary pantry staples—onion, vinegar, oil, and mustard—combine with chopped fresh rosemary to enhance the flavor of this simple baked chicken. Don't have rosemary? You can use thyme, sage, or tarragon.

1   **small onion, chopped**
¼   **cup red-wine vinegar**
1   **tablespoon olive oil**
1   **tablespoon Dijon mustard**
1   **tablespoon chopped fresh rosemary**
2   **garlic cloves, cut into slivers**
½   **teaspoon salt**
¼   **teaspoon black pepper**
1   **whole cut-up chicken (about 3½ pounds)**

1 Preheat oven to 400°F. Line large rimmed baking sheet with nonstick foil.

2 Combine onion, vinegar, oil, mustard, rosemary, garlic, salt, and pepper in large bowl. Add chicken and toss to coat.

3 Arrange chicken in single layer in baking pan, skin side up. Spoon onion mixture remaining in bowl on top of chicken. Bake until chicken is browned and cooked through (do not turn), about 45 minutes. Remove skin before eating.

3   **SmartPoints value per serving** (⅙ of chicken): 188 Cal, 6 g Total Fat, 1 g Sat Fat, 253 mg Sod, 2 g Total Carb, 1 g Sugar, 0 g Fib, 28 g Prot.

Freestyle it

Prepare some roasted vegetables along with the chicken. Place broccoli florets, sliced zucchini, yellow squash, or bell peppers on a rimmed sheet pan. Spray lightly with olive oil nonstick spray, sprinkle with salt and pepper, and toss to coat. They'll be done in about 20 minutes.

Sheet-pan cheat sheet

Sheet-pan dinners are the ultimate in quick, tasty meals. Everything (protein, vegetables, even potatoes) cooks in one pan for convenience and easy cleanup. And the flat, hot surface encourages caramelization, that tasty alchemy that gives us a gorgeously browned, naturally sweet crust on food. What's not to love?

Equipment check

- For home cooking, a standard sheet pan (aka baking tray or baking sheet) measures 13 by 18 inches with a 1-inch rim. For smaller meals and tasks, a 9 by 13-inch sheet pan is also useful. Pans measuring 18 by 26 inches (sometimes called full-size sheet pans) are generally used only in professional kitchens.

- Don't confuse a cookie sheet with a baking sheet; cookie sheets are flat, with no rim, so they're not practical for foods like meats and vegetables, which release juices while cooking.

- Most cooks have at least one sheet pan, but should you invest in a new one? Maybe. If your current pan sports years of burnt-on residue and doesn't come clean with scouring, consider replacing it. Foods are more likely to stick to a pan that's not perfectly clean, and the dark color can cause delicate foods like cookies and biscuits to scorch more easily.

- A sheet pan is one of the least expensive cooking vessels; even a top-quality one won't set you back too much. Opt for heavy aluminum pans over nonstick ones for durability and versatility.

Baking tips

- For easy cleanup, line the baking sheet with aluminum foil or, if the recipe doesn't require broiling or oven temperatures over 450°F, parchment paper.

- What's the ideal oven temperature for sheet-pan dinners? Most recipes will specify, but if you're improvising you can figure 400°F to 425°F for fish and other delicate ingredients like soft vegetables, and 425°F to 450°F for poultry, meats, and sturdy root vegetables.

- The best sheet-pan strategies often involve beginning the roasting process with dense ingredients like carrots and potatoes for the first few minutes of cooking, then adding foods like tomatoes and proteins for the final leg.

- To crisp ingredients like chicken thighs or potatoes, or to up the caramelization of your dish, turn on the broiler for the final few minutes of cooking. Just be sure to watch the food carefully: The intense heat of broiling can char your dinner very quickly!

- Add fresh herbs or a squeeze of lemon or lime at the end of cooking for bright flavor. Chopped toasted nuts will give you great crunch.

Rosemary-
prosciutto
chicken with
potatoes

Rosemary-prosciutto chicken with potatoes

Gluten Free   Serves 4

Tomatoes on the vine make a pretty presentation for this dish, but if you can only find regular cherry or grape tomatoes, the recipe will still turn out great.

1	**pound red potatoes, scrubbed and thinly sliced**
4	**garlic cloves, thinly sliced**
3	**large sprigs plus 4 small sprigs fresh rosemary**
1	**tablespoon plus 1 teaspoon olive oil**
¾	**teaspoon salt**
½	**teaspoon black pepper**
4	**(5-ounce) skinless boneless chicken breasts**
4	**thin slices prosciutto (about 2 ounces)**
½	**pound cherry tomatoes on the vine**

1 Preheat oven to 400°F. Spray large rimmed sheet pan with nonstick spray.

2 Place potatoes, garlic, and large rosemary sprigs in prepared pan. Drizzle with 1 tablespoon oil; sprinkle with ½ teaspoon salt and ¼ teaspoon pepper and toss to coat. Spread evenly in pan and roast 10 minutes.

3 Meanwhile, sprinkle chicken with remaining ¼ teaspoon salt and remaining ¼ teaspoon pepper. Top each breast with 1 slice of prosciutto, folded into thirds; tuck 1 small rosemary sprig under each slice of prosciutto.

4 Remove pan from oven and carefully place chicken on top of potatoes. Roast 15 minutes.

5 Remove pan from oven and place tomatoes in pan. Drizzle tomatoes with remaining 1 teaspoon oil and continue roasting until chicken is cooked through and potatoes are tender, about 10 minutes.

5 **SmartPoints value per serving** (1 chicken breast, about ½ cup potatoes, and about 6 cherry tomatoes): 355 Cal, 12 g Total Fat, 3 g Sat Fat, 991 mg Sod, 22 g Total Carb, 3 g Sugar, 3 g Fib, 40 g Prot.

Let's do this together

"I do not like UFOs in my freezer," says WW member René Falgout. She labels everything she freezes with the name of the dish, the date, and the SmartPoints value to prevent shuffling through a freezer full of Unidentified Frozen Objects to find what she's looking for!

Roasted Greek-style chicken and vegetables

Gluten Free   Serves 4

Looking for the easiest one-pan chicken dinner? This is it! Made with foods you've probably got on hand, this garlicky, lemony dish will see you through on weeknights when you need a flavorful, fast, and satisfying family meal.

5	**teaspoons olive oil**
3	**garlic cloves, chopped**
1	**tablespoon lemon juice**
1½	**teaspoons dried oregano**
½	**teaspoon salt**
¼	**teaspoon black pepper**
2	**small zucchini, cut into ¼-inch slices**
1	**pint cherry tomatoes, halved**
1	**(14-ounce) can water-packed artichoke hearts, drained and halved**
4	**(5-ounce) skinless boneless chicken breasts**
2	**teaspoons grated lemon zest**

1 Preheat oven to 450°F. Spray large rimmed sheet pan with nonstick spray.

2 Stir together 4 teaspoons oil, the garlic, the lemon juice, oregano, salt, and pepper in large bowl. Add zucchini, tomatoes, and artichoke hearts, tossing until coated evenly. With slotted spoon, transfer vegetables to prepared pan, spreading to form even layer at one side of pan. Add chicken to bowl and turn until coated with remaining lemon-herb mixture. Place in pan alongside vegetables in one layer.

3 Roast chicken and vegetables, stirring vegetables once, until vegetables are tender and chicken is cooked through, about 20 minutes. Drizzle remaining 1 teaspoon oil over vegetables; sprinkle with the lemon zest and toss until coated. Transfer chicken and vegetables to serving platter; drizzle with any pan juices.

SmartPoints value per serving (1 chicken breast and 1 cup vegetables): 242 Cal, 9 g Total Fat, 2 g Sat Fat, 638 mg Sod, 14 g Total Carb, 5 g Sugar, 5 g Fib, 30 g Prot.

Cook's tip
Use thawed frozen artichoke hearts in this recipe if you prefer. Cut each one in half before tossing with the oil mixture.

Chicken vegetable udon soup

Serves 6

Udon noodles are Japanese wheat noodles. If you can't find them, you can use soba noodles, rice noodles, or even spaghetti in this recipe. The garlic and ginger make the broth flavorful, and the fresh veggies give the soup a bright, vibrant flavor.

1	teaspoon canola oil
1	tablespoon minced peeled fresh ginger
2	garlic cloves, minced
1	pound skinless boneless chicken breast, cut into ½-inch strips
1	(32-ounce) carton chicken broth
3	tablespoons sake
2	tablespoons soy sauce
1	cup shiitake mushrooms, stems removed and caps sliced
6	scallions, chopped
1	carrot, thinly sliced on diagonal
4	ounces udon noodles, cooked according to package directions and drained
¼	cup lightly packed fresh cilantro leaves

1 Heat oil in large saucepan over medium-high heat. Add ginger and garlic. Cook, stirring constantly, until fragrant, about 30 seconds. Add chicken, stirring to coat. Stir in broth, sake, and soy sauce; bring to simmer.

2 Reduce heat to medium-low and simmer, covered, until chicken is cooked through, about 10 minutes. Add mushrooms, scallions, and carrot. Simmer, covered, until vegetables are tender, about 5 minutes longer. Stir in noodles and cilantro.

3 **SmartPoints value per serving** (1 generous cup): 225 Cal, 4 g Total Fat, 1 g Sat Fat, 834 mg Sod, 20 g Total Carb, 2 g Sugar, 2 g Fib, 24 g Prot.

Chicken with fresh tomato sauce

Gluten Free   Serves 4

You make the sauce for this simple chicken dish in the same pan the chicken cooks in, so cleanup is easy. The balsamic vinegar lends tangy sweetness to the tomato sauce, and fresh basil stirred in at the end makes it taste like summer—even if it's not!

4 **(5-ounce) skinless boneless chicken breasts**

2 **teaspoons chopped fresh rosemary**

½ **teaspoon salt**

¼ **teaspoon black pepper**

1 **teaspoon olive oil**

1 **large shallot, minced**

1 **garlic clove, minced**

3 **tablespoons balsamic vinegar**

6 **plum tomatoes, diced**

¼ **cup chicken broth**

¼ **cup chopped fresh basil**

1 Sprinkle chicken with rosemary, salt, and pepper. Heat oil in large nonstick skillet over medium heat. Add chicken to skillet. Cook, turning occasionally, until chicken is cooked through, about 8 minutes. Transfer to platter and keep warm.

2 Add shallot and garlic to skillet; cook, stirring often, until softened, about 2 minutes. Add vinegar, stirring with wooden spoon to scrape up browned bits from bottom of pan, and cook until vinegar is almost evaporated, about 2 minutes. Stir in tomatoes and chicken broth; bring to boil. Reduce heat and simmer, uncovered, until tomatoes just begin to soften, about 3 minutes. Stir in basil. Spoon sauce over chicken.

 SmartPoints value per serving (1 chicken breast and about ¾ cup sauce): 219 Cal, 5 g Total Fat, 1 g Sat Fat, 409 mg Sod, 8 g Total Carb, 5 g Sugar, 2 g Fib, 33 g Prot.

Cook's tip
Sprinkle each serving with 1 tablespoon of grated Parmesan cheese for an additional 1 SmartPoints.

**Chicken with fresh
tomato sauce**

Chicken and eggplant
stir-fry with snow peas

Chicken and eggplant stir-fry with snow peas

Serves 4

One key to a great stir-fry is to start with a hot pan. When food is added to a sizzling pan, it caramelizes almost immediately, developing that crusty browning that tastes so delicious. Keep the food moving, though, so it doesn't brown too much!

½   **cup chicken broth**

¼   **cup soy sauce**

3   **tablespoons mirin**

2   **teaspoons cornstarch**

2¼ **teaspoons Asian (dark) sesame oil**

1   **pound skinless boneless chicken breast, cut into ½-inch cubes**

¼   **teaspoon salt**

2   **Japanese eggplants, cut into ½-inch slices**

2   **garlic cloves, minced**

1   **tablespoon minced peeled fresh ginger**

6   **ounces snow peas, trimmed**

3   **scallions, thinly sliced**

1 Whisk together broth, soy sauce, mirin, cornstarch, and ¼ teaspoon oil. Set aside.

2 Sprinkle chicken with salt. Heat large deep skillet or wok over high heat until drop of water sizzles in pan. Add 1 teaspoon oil and swirl to coat pan. Add chicken; stir-fry until chicken is lightly browned, about 3 minutes. Transfer to plate.

3 Heat remaining 1 teaspoon oil in pan. Add eggplant, garlic, and ginger; stir-fry until eggplant is softened, about 3 minutes. Whisk sauce again and add to skillet with chicken, snow peas, and scallions. Cook, stirring constantly, until sauce comes to boil and thickens and peas are crisp-tender, 1–2 minutes.

1 **SmartPoints value per serving** (1½ cups): 222 Cal, 6 g Total Fat, 1 g Sat Fat, 1,195 mg Sod, 9 g Total Carb, 3 g Sugar, 3 g Fib, 30 g Prot.

Let's do this together

WW member Nancy Kunak takes a spin class at her local YMCA on Saturday mornings and does her shopping afterward. "It helps me make better decisions," she says. "I was just sweating for an hour and it would cancel out my productive workout if I bought unhealthy foods!"

Chicken vegetable noodle bowl

Serves 4

If you can't find precooked soba noodles for this recipe, cook 4 ounces of dry soba noodles according to the package directions; it only takes about 5 minutes.

2	**teaspoons finely chopped peeled fresh ginger**
¾	**pound skinless boneless chicken breast cutlets, cut into ½-inch pieces**
1	**teaspoon salt**
4	**cups chicken broth**
1	**large carrot, shredded**
1	**red bell pepper, thinly sliced**
6	**thin scallions, thinly sliced**
1	**cup frozen shelled edamame**
3	**cups baby spinach**
1	**(7.1-ounce) package precooked soba noodles**
3	**tablespoons ponzu sauce or soy sauce**
1	**teaspoon (Asian) dark hot sesame oil**
½	**cup fresh cilantro leaves**

1 Spray large Dutch oven with nonstick spray and set over medium-high heat. Add ginger and cook, stirring constantly, just until fragrant, 30 seconds. Add chicken and ½ teaspoon salt; cook, stirring constantly, just until chicken is no longer pink, 2–3 minutes.

2 Increase heat to high; add broth, carrot, bell pepper, scallions, and edamame. Bring to boil.

3 Stir in spinach, noodles, ponzu sauce, and remaining ½ teaspoon salt; cook until heated through, 2 minutes. Remove from heat and stir in oil. Ladle soup evenly into 4 bowls and sprinkle with cilantro.

(3) **SmartPoints value per serving** (2¼ cups): 289 Cal, 8 g Total Fat, 1 g Sat Fat, 1,152 mg Sod, 23 g Total Carb, 6 g Sugar, 4 g Fib, 33 g Prot.

Let's do this together
Shelled edamame is a delicious way to add protein to soups like this one, but edamame in the pod is great, too. Kathleen Messersmith finds that it comes in handy when she feels the need to mindlessly eat. "It takes time to get them out of the pods," she says. And the best part: 0 SmartPoints!

Chicken vegetable noodle bowl

Lemon-rosemary chicken with radicchio

Gluten Free   **Serves 4**

In this roasted version of radicchio, it changes from vibrant red to tarnished brown, but the sweet, assertive flavor it develops makes up for the unattractive color.

Grated zest of 1 lemon

2   **garlic cloves, minced**

2   **teaspoons finely chopped fresh rosemary**

¾   **teaspoon salt**

½   **teaspoon black pepper**

4   **(6- to 7-ounce) skin-on bone-in chicken thighs**

1   **tablespoon balsamic vinegar**

2   **teaspoons extra-virgin olive oil**

1   **large head radicchio, cut into 4 wedges**

1 Preheat oven to 425°F.

2 Stir together lemon zest, garlic, rosemary, ½ teaspoon salt, and ¼ teaspoon pepper in small bowl. Spread evenly onto chicken and under skin of each thigh. Spray large heavy ovenproof skillet with nonstick spray and set over medium-high heat. Add chicken, skin side down, and cook until chicken is golden, about 5 minutes.

3 Meanwhile, whisk together vinegar, oil, remaining ¼ teaspoon salt, and remaining ¼ teaspoon pepper in large bowl. Add radicchio and toss to coat.

4 Transfer chicken to plate; drain and discard fat from pan. Return chicken to skillet and add radicchio, cut sides up. Transfer skillet to oven and roast until radicchio is tender and instant-read thermometer inserted into thigh registers 165°F, about 20 minutes. With tongs, transfer chicken and radicchio to platter; drizzle top with pan juices. Remove skin before eating.

5 **SmartPoints value per serving** (1 chicken thigh, 1 wedge radicchio, and about 2 teaspoons pan juices): 247 Cal, 9 g Total Fat, 2 g Sat Fat, 613 mg Sod, 5 g Total Carb, 1 g Sugar, 1 g Fib, 34 g Prot.

Freestyle it
Add some color to your plate and offset the bitterness of the radicchio by serving this dish with a vegetable that lends a touch of sweetness. Try roasted butternut squash, fennel, or carrots.

Slow cooker balsamic-braised chicken with kale

Serves 4

3	**tablespoons all-purpose flour**
¾	**teaspoon salt**
¼	**teaspoon black pepper**
4	**(6-ounce) skinless bone-in chicken thighs, trimmed**
1	**tablespoon olive oil**
4	**red onions, thinly sliced**
1	**(14½-ounce) can diced tomatoes**
½	**cup chicken broth**
2	**tablespoons balsamic vinegar**
1	**teaspoon fresh thyme**
1	**(5-ounce) container baby kale**

Lemon wedges

1 Mix together flour, salt, and pepper on sheet of wax paper. Coat chicken with seasoned flour, shaking off excess.

2 Heat oil in large skillet over medium heat. Add chicken and cook until browned, about 4 minutes per side. Transfer to plate. Add onions to skillet and cook, stirring often, until onion is browned, about 10 minutes. Transfer onions to 5- or 6-quart slow cooker.

3 Add tomatoes, broth, vinegar, and thyme to slow cooker and stir to mix well. Place chicken in slow cooker and spoon onion mixture over. Cover and cook until chicken is fork-tender, about 4 hours on low.

4 Transfer chicken to plate and keep warm. Stir kale into slow cooker and let stand, uncovered, until kale is wilted, about 5 minutes. Divide chicken evenly among 4 plates. Top with vegetable mixture. Serve with lemon wedges.

5   **SmartPoints value per serving** (1 chicken thigh and ½ cup vegetables): 344 Cal, 11 g Total Fat, 2 g Sat Fat, 855 mg Sod, 23 g Total Carb, 9 g Sugar, 5 g Fib, 38 g Prot.

Let's do this together

WW member Brianna Engebretsen uses her slow cooker as a big time-saver. "I make chicken, pot roast, or chili," she says. "I love that I can put things in there and come back a few hours later to a cooked dinner."

Slow cooker chicken stew with roasted-pepper rouille

Gluten Free   Serves 4

Browning the chicken in a skillet before it goes into the slow cooker adds a step to this recipe, but it's worth it for the rich, complex flavor it gives the finished dish.

4   **(6-ounce) skinless bone-in chicken thighs, trimmed**

1   **teaspoon dried thyme**

½   **teaspoon salt**

¼   **teaspoon black pepper**

1½ **teaspoons olive oil**

2   **small fennel bulbs, sliced**

2   **leeks, halved lengthwise and sliced (white and pale green parts only)**

4   **large garlic cloves, finely chopped**

Large pinch saffron threads, crushed

⅔   **cup dry white wine or dry vermouth**

1   **tablespoon tomato paste**

1   **(14½-ounce) can diced tomatoes**

½   **cup chicken broth**

2   **(3-inch) strips orange zest**

Rouille

½   **cup drained water-packed roasted red peppers, patted dry with paper towel**

3   **tablespoons reduced-fat mayonnaise**

1   **garlic clove, crushed through a press**

½   **teaspoon hot sauce, or to taste**

⅛   **teaspoon salt**

1 Sprinkle chicken with thyme, salt, and pepper. Heat oil in large skillet over medium-high heat. Add chicken and cook until golden brown, about 3 minutes per side. Transfer to 4- or 5-quart slow cooker.

2 Reduce heat to medium. Add fennel and leeks to skillet; cook, covered, stirring occasionally, until vegetables are tender, about 5 minutes. Add chopped garlic and saffron; cook, stirring frequently, until fragrant, about 30 seconds. Add wine and tomato paste; bring to boil, stirring until blended. Stir in diced tomatoes, broth, and orange zest. Pour tomato mixture over chicken. Cover and cook just until chicken is fork-tender, 2½–3 hours on high or 5–6 hours on low.

3 Meanwhile, to make rouille, combine roasted peppers, 2 tablespoons mayonnaise, the crushed garlic, hot sauce, and salt in mini–food processor; pulse until smooth. Transfer sauce to small bowl; stir in remaining 1 tablespoon mayonnaise. Taste and season with additional hot sauce, if desired. Cover and refrigerate.

4 Discard orange zest from chicken. Place 1 chicken thigh in each of 4 large shallow bowls and spoon vegetables and sauce over and around chicken. Top each serving with dollop of rouille.

7 **SmartPoints value per serving** (1 chicken thigh, ½ cup vegetables and sauce, and scant 2 tablespoons rouille): 390 Cal, 12 g Total Fat, 2 g Sat Fat, 1,064 mg Sod, 29 g Total Carb, 7 g Sugar, 6 g Fib, 37 g Prot.

Braised chicken with potatoes and artichokes

Serves 4

We'll be honest: This isn't the prettiest dish, but if you love a good hearty weeknight chicken dinner that's full of flavor and cooks in one pan, this is what you're looking for. Add a green salad and you're done!

4	**(5-ounce) skinless boneless chicken thighs, trimmed**
½	**teaspoon salt**
¼	**teaspoon black pepper**
2	**tablespoons all-purpose flour**
2	**teaspoons olive oil**
8	**baby potatoes, quartered (about 5 ounces)**
1	**small red onion, finely chopped**
½	**cup chicken broth**
1	**(9-ounce) package frozen artichoke hearts, thawed**
2	**tablespoons white balsamic vinegar**
2	**teaspoons minced fresh rosemary**
1	**tablespoon lemon juice**

1 Sprinkle chicken with salt and pepper, then with flour, shaking off excess.

2 Spray large skillet with nonstick spray and set over medium-high heat. Add chicken and cook, turning once, until chicken is browned, about 8 minutes. Transfer chicken to plate.

3 Add oil to skillet. Add potatoes and onion and cook, stirring often, until onion is softened, about 5 minutes. Add broth to skillet and bring to boil, stirring with wooden spoon to scrape up browned bits from bottom of skillet. Add artichokes, vinegar, 1 teaspoon rosemary, and the chicken with any accumulated juices to skillet.

4 Cover and simmer until potatoes are tender, turning chicken once, about 15 minutes. Remove from heat and stir in lemon juice. Sprinkle with remaining 1 teaspoon rosemary.

5 Divide chicken and vegetables evenly among 4 plates.

 SmartPoints value per serving (1 chicken thigh and about ½ cup vegetables): 306 Cal, 9 g Total Fat, 2 g Sat Fat, 562 mg Sod, 25 g Total Carb, 5 g Sugar, 5 g Fib, 32 g Prot.

Cook's tip

Those browned bits we tell you to scrape up from the bottom of the skillet in this recipe (and in many others) are what the French call "fond." It's created from the caramelization of foods as they brown, and though you won't actually see it in the finished dish, it imparts a wonderful flavor.

Lemon chicken with white beans and stuffed peppers

Lemon chicken with white beans and stuffed peppers

Gluten Free   Serves 4

Tomato-stuffed bell peppers, lemony chicken, and white beans flavored with basil and olives—all cooked in one pan—make this dish a go-to weeknight meal.

2	red, orange, or yellow bell peppers
4	small tomatoes, cored and halved
3	garlic cloves, sliced
1	small red onion, cut into 8 wedges
4	(5-ounce) skinless boneless chicken thighs
½	teaspoon dried oregano
¾	teaspoon salt
¼	teaspoon black pepper
4	lemon slices
1	tablespoon plus 1 teaspoon olive oil
1	(15-ounce) can cannellini (white kidney) beans, rinsed and drained
⅓	cup lightly packed fresh basil leaves, roughly torn
8	black olives, pitted and coarsely chopped

1 Preheat oven to 400°F. Spray large rimmed sheet pan with nonstick spray.

2 Slice bell peppers in half lengthwise, cutting through middle of each stem, leaving stems intact; scrape out seeds. Place 1 tomato half inside each pepper half; sprinkle with garlic. Place bell peppers and remaining 4 tomato halves on one side of prepared pan.

3 Place onion on other side of pan; arrange chicken on top of onion. Sprinkle peppers and chicken with oregano, ½ teaspoon salt, and ⅛ teaspoon black pepper. Place lemon slices on top of chicken. Drizzle peppers and chicken with 1 tablespoon oil.

4 Roast until chicken is cooked through and edges of peppers are lightly browned, 30–35 minutes.

5 Remove pan from oven and transfer chicken and stuffed peppers to plate. Add remaining 1 teaspoon oil, remaining ¼ teaspoon salt, and remaining ⅛ teaspoon black pepper to pan. Using wooden spoon, break up tomatoes; add beans and stir to combine with onion. Return chicken to pan and roast until beans are heated through, about 5 minutes. Stir basil and olives into bean mixture. Serve chicken with stuffed peppers and bean mixture.

5 **SmartPoints value per serving** (1 chicken thigh, 1 stuffed pepper, and about ½ cup bean mixture): 346 Cal, 12 g Total Fat, 2 g Sat Fat, 998 mg Sod, 26 g Total Carb, 5 g Sugar, 7 g Fib, 36 g Prot.

Roast chermoula chicken with butternut squash

Gluten Free   Serves 4

To add a green vegetable to this one-pan dish, stir 3 cups packed baby spinach into the vegetables in the pan until wilted just before serving.

1	**pound fresh peeled and cubed butternut squash**
3	**large shallots, each cut into 6 wedges**
1	**tablespoon plus 2 teaspoons olive oil**
¾	**teaspoon salt**
½	**teaspoon black pepper**
½	**cup packed fresh cilantro leaves**
2	**tablespoons packed fresh parsley leaves**
2	**garlic cloves, chopped**
½	**jalapeño pepper, seeded and chopped**
1½	**teaspoons ground cumin**
1	**teaspoon lemon juice**
	Pinch saffron
4	**(5-ounce) skinless boneless chicken thighs**

1 Preheat oven to 425°F. Spray large rimmed sheet pan with nonstick spray.

2 Place squash and shallots in prepared pan; drizzle with 1 tablespoon oil, sprinkle with ¼ teaspoon salt and ¼ teaspoon pepper, and toss to coat. Roast 10 minutes.

3 Meanwhile, combine cilantro, parsley, garlic, jalapeño, cumin, lemon juice, saffron, remaining 2 teaspoons oil, remaining ½ teaspoon salt, and remaining ¼ teaspoon pepper in mini–food processor and pulse until mixture is finely chopped.

4 Make 3 diagonal slits across top of each chicken thigh; spread cilantro mixture over chicken and into slits.

5 Remove pan from oven and carefully place chicken on top of vegetables. Roast until chicken is cooked through and squash and shallots are tender, 20–25 minutes.

 5 **SmartPoints value per serving** (1 chicken thigh and generous ½ cup vegetables): 308 Cal, 12 g Total Fat, 2 g Sat Fat, 584 mg Sod, 21 g Total Carb, 6 g Sugar, 4 g Fib, 30 g Prot.

Let's do this together

Using just one pan in recipes like this one is a time-saving trick WW member Tracey Steckmeister uses often. "When I find myself with limited time, I look up recipes using one of my go-to ingredients—chicken, shrimp, and ground turkey—that require only a sheet pan or a single pot," she says.

Turkey, red bean, and chipotle pepper chili

Gluten Free   Serves 4

1   tablespoon olive oil
1   onion, chopped
1   red bell pepper, chopped
4   garlic cloves, minced
1   pound ground skinless turkey breast
1   (28-ounce) can diced tomatoes
1   (15½-ounce) can red kidney beans, rinsed and drained
2   teaspoons chipotle chile powder
2   teaspoons ground cumin
1   teaspoon dried oregano
½   teaspoon salt
4   tablespoons plain low-fat Greek yogurt
Chopped fresh cilantro
Sliced scallions
Lime wedges

1 Heat oil in Dutch oven over medium heat. Add onion, bell pepper, and garlic; cook, stirring often, until vegetables are softened, about 5 minutes.

2 Add turkey to pot and cook, breaking it apart with wooden spoon, until turkey is no longer pink, about 3 minutes. Stir in tomatoes, beans, chile powder, cumin, oregano, and salt and bring to boil. Reduce heat and simmer, covered, until vegetables are tender, about 30 minutes.

3 Ladle chili evenly into 4 bowls; top with yogurt. Sprinkle with cilantro and scallions and serve with lime wedges.

1 **SmartPoints value per serving** (about 1⅓ cups chili and 1 tablespoon yogurt): 323 Cal, 7 g Total Fat, 1 g Sat Fat, 998 mg Sod, 31 g Total Carb, 10 g Sugar, 9 g Fib, 37 g Prot.

Let's do this together
Double up when you make this recipe and freeze part of it for later. WW member Sheri Friedman does this often. "I freeze food both in family-size and single-serving containers," she says. "Larger quantities are for family or for entertaining, and the single-serves are just for me."

Tandoori chicken skewers with roasted vegetables

Gluten Free   Serves 4

Better than takeout and ready in about 45 minutes, this spicy chicken-and-veggie dinner tastes authentically Indian. To skip the skewers, place the chicken pieces on top of the vegetables and roast, stirring the chicken instead of turning the skewers.

¼   **cup plain fat-free yogurt**

2   **teaspoons grated peeled fresh ginger**

2   **garlic cloves, crushed through a press**

2   **teaspoons garam masala**

1   **teaspoon turmeric**

¾   **teaspoon ground cumin**

¾   **teaspoon salt**

¼   **teaspoon cayenne**

4   **(5-ounce) skinless boneless chicken thighs, cut into 1½-inch pieces**

1   **tablespoon canola oil**

1   **teaspoon mustard seeds**

1   **teaspoon nigella seeds (optional)**

¼   **teaspoon black pepper**

1   **large zucchini, halved lengthwise and cut into 2-inch pieces (about ½ pound)**

1   **head cauliflower, cut into 12 wedges (about 1½ pounds)**

1   **red onion, cut into wedges**

Chopped fresh cilantro

Lemon wedges

1 Combine yogurt, ginger, garlic, 1½ teaspoons garam masala, ¼ teaspoon turmeric, the cumin, ½ teaspoon salt, and the cayenne in large zip-close plastic bag. Add chicken, squeeze out air, and seal bag; and turn to coat chicken. Refrigerate at least 2 hours or up to 5 hours.

2 Preheat oven to 425°F. Spray large rimmed sheet pan with nonstick spray. Stir together oil, remaining ½ teaspoon garam masala, the mustard seeds, nigella seeds, if using, remaining ¾ teaspoon turmeric, the pepper, and remaining ¼ teaspoon salt in large bowl. Add zucchini, cauliflower, and onion and toss to coat. Spread into prepared pan and roast 10 minutes.

3 Meanwhile, remove chicken from marinade; discard marinade. Thread chicken onto 4 (12-inch) metal skewers (if using wooden skewers, soak in water 20 minutes prior to use to prevent charring).

4 Remove pan from oven and place skewers on top of vegetables. Roast 10 minutes. Turn skewers and stir vegetables. Return to oven and continue roasting until chicken is cooked through and vegetables are tender, about 10 minutes longer.

5 Divide vegetables and skewers evenly among 4 plates; sprinkle with cilantro and serve with lemon wedges.

SmartPoints value per serving (1 skewer and 1 cup vegetables): 269 Cal, 10 g Total Fat, 2 g Sat Fat, 633 mg Sod, 13 g Total Carb, 7 g Sugar, 5 g Fib, 33 g Prot.

**Tandoori chicken skewers
with roasted vegetables**

Lentil and chorizo
soup with kale

Lentil and chorizo soup with kale

Gluten Free   Serves 4

Chorizo is typically made with pork and flavored with paprika. It can be spicy or not, and it comes cured and fully cooked or raw. If you have trouble finding chicken chorizo, you can make this hearty soup with any type of chorizo, andouille, or kielbasa.

1	onion, chopped
2	fully cooked chicken chorizo sausages, diced (6 ounces)
4	garlic cloves, minced
1	(½-pound) bunch kale, stems discarded and leaves coarsely chopped
3	cups chicken broth
3	cups water
1	cup brown lentils, picked over and rinsed
¾	teaspoon salt
2	large plum tomatoes, diced
¼	teaspoon smoked paprika

1 Spray Dutch oven with nonstick spray and set over medium heat. Add onion and chorizo and cook, stirring occasionally, until onion is golden, about 10 minutes. Add garlic and cook, stirring constantly, until fragrant, 30 seconds. Add kale and cook, stirring often, until kale is wilted. Stir in broth, water, and lentils. Bring to boil; reduce heat and simmer, covered, until lentils are tender, about 45 minutes. Stir in salt.

2 Meanwhile, stir together tomatoes and paprika in medium microwaveable bowl. Cover with wax paper and microwave on high until heated through, about 1½ minutes. Serve soup topped with tomato mixture.

3 **SmartPoints value per serving** (2 cups soup and ¼ cup tomato mixture): 326 Cal, 6 g Total Fat, 2 g Sat Fat, 1,064 mg Sod, 42 g Total Carb, 5 g Sugar, 8 g Fib, 27 g Prot.

Let's do this together

Soups like this one are one of WW member René Falgout's go-to meals for weekend cooking. "I cook a very large batch of soup," she explains. "Most soups freeze really well, so I cook enough to make as many as six meals for my family."

Thai turkey and broccoli stir-fry

Serves 4

Sweet, spicy, salty, crunchy—this stir-fry has it all! It uses turkey cutlets, but you can substitute skinless boneless chicken breasts if you prefer.

3   **tablespoons reduced-sodium soy sauce**

2   **tablespoons lime juice**

1   **tablespoon Asian fish sauce**

1   **tablespoon packed brown sugar**

1½   **teaspoons canola oil**

1   **pound turkey breast cutlets, cut into ½-inch strips**

1   **shallot, finely chopped**

1   **jalapeño pepper, seeded and minced**

1   **small bunch broccoli (about ¾ pound), stems trimmed and sliced, tops cut into small florets**

½   **cup water**

1   **cup shredded carrot**

⅓   **cup chopped fresh cilantro**

2   **tablespoons unsalted roasted peanuts, chopped**

1 Stir together soy sauce, lime juice, fish sauce, and brown sugar in small bowl.

2 Heat 1 teaspoon oil in large nonstick skillet over medium heat. Add turkey and cook, stirring constantly until turkey is no longer pink, about 3 minutes. Transfer turkey to plate. Add remaining ½ teaspoon oil to skillet. Add shallot and jalapeño and cook, stirring constantly, until fragrant, about 1 minute. Add to plate with turkey.

3 Add broccoli and water to skillet. Cook, stirring often, until broccoli is crisp-tender and water evaporates, about 3 minutes. Add carrot, turkey mixture, and soy sauce mixture to skillet. Cook, stirring often, until turkey is heated through, about 2 minutes. Remove skillet from heat and stir in cilantro. Sprinkle with peanuts.

2   **SmartPoints value per serving** (1½ cups): 241 Cal, 6 g Total Fat, 1 g Sat Fat, 910 mg Sod, 16 g Total Carb, 8 g Sugar, 4 g Fib, 32 g Prot.

Freestyle it

Add or substitute almost any quick-cooking vegetable to this recipe. Snow peas, yellow squash, zucchini, thin green beans, asparagus, or baby bok choy would all work well.

Thai turkey and broccoli stir-fry

Turkey-tomatillo
chili

Turkey-tomatillo chili

Gluten Free   Serves 6

Grilled Italian bread makes a crunchy accompaniment to this chili. A one ounce slice per serving will add 2 SmartPoints value.

2	teaspoons canola oil
1	onion, diced
1	red bell pepper, diced
1	large garlic clove, minced
1	pound ground skinless turkey breast
3	tablespoons chili powder
1	teaspoon ground cumin
½	teaspoon salt, or to taste
½	pound tomatillos, husks removed, rinsed, and halved
1	(4.5-ounce) can chopped green chiles
½	cup lightly packed fresh cilantro leaves
2	cups chicken broth
2	(15-ounce) cans cannellini (white kidney) beans, rinsed and drained

Lime wedges

1 Heat oil in Dutch oven over medium heat. Add onion, bell pepper, and garlic. Cook, stirring often, until vegetables are softened, about 5 minutes. Add turkey, chili powder, cumin, and salt. Increase heat to medium-high and cook, breaking it apart with wooden spoon, until turkey is browned, about 5 minutes.

2 Meanwhile, purée tomatillos, chiles, and cilantro in food processor or blender; add to turkey mixture. Stir in broth and beans; bring to boil. Reduce heat and simmer, covered, until mixture is thickened, about 45 minutes. Season to taste with additional salt, if desired. Serve with lime wedges.

1 **SmartPoints value per serving** (1¼ cups): 262 Cal, 5 g Total Fat, 1 g Sat Fat, 1,135 mg Sod, 28 g Total Carb, 4 g Sugar, 7 g Fib, 29 g Prot.

Let's do this together

WW member Kshatriya Millick can't live without her food processor. "I'll add several different chopped vegetables to a recipe, and with the food processor, prep time is only seconds," she explains. "It's allowed me to include more 0 SmartPoints vegetables to recipes by reducing my time in the kitchen."

Southwest turkey and vegetable soup

Gluten Free   Serves 6

This quick and delicious one-pot meal is loaded with fresh and satisfying 0 SmartPoints turkey breast, veggies, and beans. It's a comforting weeknight family meal, but you can also portion it out and freeze it to take to work for lunch.

2	teaspoons canola oil
1	large onion, chopped
1	pound ground skinless turkey breast
4	teaspoons hot chili powder
2	teaspoons ground cumin
1½	teaspoons oregano
¾	teaspoon salt
4	cups chicken broth
1	zucchini, quartered lengthwise and sliced
3	plum tomatoes, diced
1	cup fresh corn kernels (from 2 ears)
1	(15-ounce) can small white beans, rinsed and drained
½	cup chopped fresh cilantro
2	tablespoons fresh lime juice
	Lime wedges

1 Heat oil in Dutch oven over medium heat. Add onion and cook, stirring often, 3 minutes. Add turkey, chili powder, cumin, oregano, and salt and cook, breaking it apart with wooden spoon, until turkey is no longer pink, 6 minutes.

2 Add broth and bring to simmer. Add zucchini and tomatoes and simmer, 4 minutes. Stir in corn and beans and cook until heated through, about 2 minutes. Remove from heat and stir in cilantro and lime juice. Serve with lime wedges.

1 **SmartPoints value per serving** (1½ cups): 249 Cal, 4 g Total Fat, 1 g Sat Fat, 761 mg Sod, 29 g Total Carb, 4 g Sugar, 6 g Fib, 27 g Prot.

Cook's tip
If you don't have hot chili powder, substitute an equal amount of regular chili powder and add ⅛ teaspoon cayenne.

Tuscan sausage and bean stew

Gluten Free   Serves 4

2   teaspoons olive oil

6   ounces fully cooked Italian-style chicken or turkey sausages, diced

1   (10-ounce) package sliced mushrooms

1   small onion, chopped

2   garlic cloves, minced

2   (14½-ounce) cans diced tomatoes

1   (15½-ounce) can cannellini (white kidney) beans, rinsed and drained

1   zucchini, diced

2   teaspoons chopped fresh rosemary

2   cups baby arugula

¼   cup grated Parmesan

1 Heat oil in large skillet over medium-high heat. Add sausages and cook, stirring often, until lightly browned, about 3 minutes. Transfer to plate with slotted spoon.

2 Add mushrooms and onion to same skillet and cook, stirring often, until vegetables are softened, about 3 minutes. Add garlic and cook, stirring constantly, until fragrant, about 30 seconds.

3 Stir in reserved sausages, tomatoes, beans, zucchini, and rosemary and bring to boil. Reduce heat and simmer, until vegetables are tender, about 2 minutes. Remove from heat and stir in arugula until wilted.

4 Ladle stew into 4 bowls and top evenly with Parmesan.

3 **SmartPoints value per serving** (1½ cups stew and 1 tablespoon cheese): 255 Cal, 8 g Total Fat, 2 g Sat Fat, 1,067 mg Sod, 31 g Total Carb, 9 g Sugar, 7 g Fib, 19 g Prot.

Chapter 5

Comforting classics

Oven-barbecued chicken with mop sauce, 148

Hearty chicken with parsley dumplings, 150

All about poultry sausage, 151

Buttermilk-marinated oven-fried chicken, 152

Chicken Milanese with arugula salad, 153

Chicken ratatouille with penne, 155

Creole jambalaya, 156

Chicken and sausage paella, 157

Chicken, caramelized onion, and goat cheese pizza, 158

Stovetop cassoulet, 161

Wild mushroom and sausage risotto, 162

Chicken, corn, and black bean pizza, 164

Turkey mushroom-barley soup with dill, 165

Chicken pot pie with chive biscuits, 167

Ginger meatball and vegetable soup, 168

Very veggie turkey meat loaf, 171

Turkey, spinach, and goat cheese enchiladas, 172

Turkey, spinach, and mushroom lasagna, 174

Rigatoni with turkey bolognese, 175

Greek turkey meatballs, 177

Oven-barbecued chicken with mop sauce

Gluten Free **Serves 6**

Barbecued chicken is a family favorite, even when it's too cold—or you don't have time—to fire up the grill. This all-season recipe delivers on flavor with a sweet and spicy rub plus a tart tomatoey mop sauce. Coleslaw makes a perfect accompaniment.

3	teaspoons packed dark brown sugar
1	tablespoon paprika
1	tablespoon plus 1 teaspoon chili powder
2	teaspoons ground cumin
¼	teaspoon ground allspice
¾	teaspoon salt
1	whole cut-up chicken (about 3½ pounds)
⅓	cup ketchup
2	tablespoons apple cider vinegar
½	teaspoon Worcestershire sauce

1 Preheat oven to 425°F. Line roasting pan with foil and spray foil with nonstick spray.

2 Stir together 1 teaspoon sugar, the paprika, 1 tablespoon chili powder, the cumin, allspice, and salt in small dish. Rub mixture all over chicken to coat. Stir remaining 2 teaspoons sugar, remaining 1 teaspoon chili powder, the ketchup, vinegar, and Worcestershire sauce together in another small bowl. Set aside.

3 Place chicken in prepared pan and bake 35 minutes. Remove from oven and brush with ketchup mixture. Bake until chicken is cooked through, 10–15 minutes longer. Discard skin before eating.

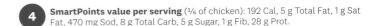

4 **SmartPoints value per serving** (⅙ of chicken): 192 Cal, 5 g Total Fat, 1 g Sat Fat, 470 mg Sod, 8 g Total Carb, 5 g Sugar, 1 g Fib, 28 g Prot.

Cook's tip
We brush on the barbecue sauce only during the last 15 minutes of baking to prevent the sweet glaze from burning. Line the pan with foil to make it easier to clean up.

Oven-barbecued chicken with mop sauce

Hearty chicken with parsley dumplings

Serves 6

Fluffy dumplings floating in an herbed chicken-and-vegetable stew is comfort food at its best. Gather friends and family around the table to enjoy this steamy supper on a frosty fall or winter evening.

1	tablespoon canola oil
1	large onion, coarsely chopped
4	garlic cloves, minced
3	celery stalks, cut into 1½-inch pieces
4	carrots, cut into 1½-inch pieces
4	cups chicken broth
2	fresh thyme sprigs
¼	teaspoon salt
¼	teaspoon black pepper
6	(½-pound) bone-in chicken breasts, skinned

Dumplings

1	large egg
⅔	cup fat-free milk
2	cups all-purpose flour
1½	teaspoons baking powder
½	teaspoon salt
1	tablespoon chopped fresh parsley

1 Heat oil in Dutch oven over medium heat. Add onion and garlic; cook, stirring occasionally, until onion is softened, about 5 minutes. Stir in celery, carrots, broth, thyme, salt, and pepper. Add chicken and bring to boil, skimming off any foam that rises to surface. Reduce heat and simmer until chicken is cooked through, about 30 minutes. Transfer chicken to plate and let cool. Separate meat from bones; discard bones.

2 To make dumplings, whisk together egg and milk in medium bowl until frothy. Whisk in 1 cup flour, the baking powder, and salt. Add remaining 1 cup flour and the parsley, stirring until it forms thick batter.

3 Return broth to simmer over medium-high heat. Reduce heat to medium. Drop batter by heaping ¼ cupfuls into broth, making total of 6 dumplings, and cook 7 minutes; carefully turn dumplings over. Cook, covered, until dumplings are light and fluffy, about 7 minutes longer.

4 Return chicken to pot and cook until heated through, about 3 minutes longer.

5 Divide chicken, dumplings, sauce, and vegetables evenly among 6 large shallow bowls.

6 **SmartPoints value per serving** (⅙ of chicken and vegetables with sauce and 1 dumpling): 525 Cal, 10 g Total Fat, 2 g Sat Fat, 1,095 mg Sod, 42 g Total Carb, 5 g Sugar, 3 g Fib, 62 g Prot.

All about poultry sausage

We love poultry sausage. It gives us the lush flavor and toothsome texture we crave from traditional pork sausage while making the most of the leanness that poultry is famous for. And a little goes a long way, imparting its savory goodness to more neutral ingredients like eggs, beans, rice, and mild veggies. Here's a rundown of what you need to know to buy the best sausage for your dishes.

Types of poultry sausage

Fresh sausage, made from uncooked ground meat, is usually sold in links. Italian sausage, sweet or spicy, is the most common type of poultry sausage, but breakfast sausages, chorizo, and some German sausages like bratwurst are sometimes available.

Bulk fresh sausage sold loose, without being stuffed into casings, is known as bulk sausage. It's convenient for recipes that mix the sausage into other ingredients, like stuffings, meatballs, pasta sauces, and more. If you can't find bulk poultry sausage, simply split fresh link sausages and remove the meat from the casing.

Precooked sausages have much longer shelf life and are easy to prepare (think of the humble hotdog!). Some sausages are cooked by smoking for extra flavor, like turkey kielbasa and andouille. Despite being ready to eat, most of these sausages will benefit from being seared or browned for extra flavor.

Cured sausages that have been salted and air-dried like pepperoni and salami are sometimes made from poultry. Their dense texture makes them perfect for slicing very thinly, and their concentrated flavor makes them excellent in small quantities in sandwiches, on pizza, and diced over salads.

What to look for in a sausage

A good poultry sausage will be made with meat, a moderate amount of fat, salt, and natural spices and flavorings. Here's what to look for on a label or ask your butcher about.

- Chicken or turkey should always be the first ingredient. Some sausage makers advertise that their products are made with "whole muscle" meat, which means scraps are kept to a minimum.

- Fat and saturated fat can vary widely in poultry sausages. Look for brands with about 7 grams of fat and 2 to 3 grams of saturated fat per 3-ounce link.

- Avoid sausages made with fillers like starches, flours, gums, hydrolyzed vegetable protein, or other additives.

- Look for sausages made without artificial preservatives, artificial nitrates and nitrites, or artificial colors and flavors.

- Beware of excess sodium in sausages if you need to control your salt intake.

Buttermilk-marinated oven-fried chicken

Serves 4

Using buttermilk as a marinade for chicken is a tried-and-true Southern technique—and they ought to know! The acidity in the buttermilk helps tenderize and add moisture to the chicken, making the finished dish one of the juiciest you'll ever enjoy.

¾	**cup low-fat buttermilk**
1	**teaspoon black pepper**
¾	**teaspoon salt**
4	**(7-ounce) bone-in chicken breasts, skinned**
⅔	**cup panko (bread crumbs)**
2	**tablespoons grated Parmesan**
1	**tablespoon paprika**
1½	**teaspoons dried sage**
1	**teaspoon dried rosemary, crushed**

1 Preheat oven to 350°F. Line baking sheet with foil and spray foil with nonstick spray.

2 Combine buttermilk, ½ teaspoon pepper, and ½ teaspoon salt in large zip-close plastic bag; add chicken. Squeeze out air and seal bag; turn to coat chicken. Refrigerate, turning bag occasionally, at least 3 hours or up to overnight.

3 Mix together panko, Parmesan, paprika, sage, rosemary, remaining ½ teaspoon pepper, and remaining ¼ teaspoon salt in shallow dish.

4 Remove chicken from marinade; discard marinade. Coat chicken, one piece at a time, in bread-crumb mixture. Place chicken on prepared baking sheet and bake 30 minutes. Remove baking sheet from oven and lightly spray chicken with olive oil spray. Return chicken to oven and bake until cooked through and crumbs are golden, about 15 minutes longer.

 SmartPoints value per serving (1 chicken breast): 314 Cal, 7 g Total Fat, 2 g Sat Fat, 782 mg Sod, 16 g Total Carb, 3 g Sugar, 1 g Fib, 43 g Prot.

Freestyle it
Continue the Southern theme in this meal by serving the chicken with braised collard greens. Cook chopped onion and garlic in a saucepan coated with nonstick spray; add sliced collards and water and simmer until tender, about 20 minutes. Season with salt and red pepper flakes.

Chicken Milanese with arugula salad

Serves 4

Peppery arugula topped with a tart lemon dressing is the perfect accompaniment to crispy crumb-and-cheese-crusted chicken cutlets.

3½ **tablespoons lemon juice**

1 **tablespoon plus
½ teaspoon olive oil**

¾ **teaspoon salt**

¾ **teaspoon black pepper**

4 **cups loosely packed
baby arugula**

½ **fennel bulb, very thinly
sliced (about 1 cup)**

1 **cup thinly sliced red onion**

1 **cup grape tomatoes,
quartered**

4 **(5-ounce) skinless boneless
chicken breast cutlets**

2 **tablespoons all-purpose
flour**

⅓ **cup plain dried bread
crumbs**

1 **large egg plus 1 large
egg white**

2 **tablespoons finely chopped
fresh flat-leaf parsley**

2 **tablespoons grated
pecorino Romano**

1 **tablespoon butter**

1 To make dressing, whisk together 1½ tablespoons lemon juice, 1 tablespoon oil, ¼ teaspoon salt, and ¼ teaspoon pepper in large bowl. Place arugula, fennel, onion, and tomatoes on top of dressing (do not mix). Set aside.

2 Sprinkle chicken with remaining ½ teaspoon salt and remaining ½ teaspoon pepper.

3 Spread flour and bread crumbs on separate sheets of wax paper. Whisk together egg, egg white, parsley, and pecorino Romano in large shallow bowl.

4 Coat chicken with flour, one piece at a time, shaking off excess. Dip into egg mixture, then lightly coat with bread crumbs.

5 Coat large nonstick skillet with remaining ½ teaspoon oil and set over medium heat. Add ½ tablespoon butter and heat until melted. Add 2 chicken breasts and cook until crumb coating is golden and chicken is cooked through, about 3 minutes per side; transfer chicken to plate. Keep warm. Repeat with remaining ½ tablespoon butter and remaining 2 chicken breasts.

6 Toss salad with dressing until coated evenly. Place chicken on 4 plates; sprinkle evenly with remaining 2 tablespoons lemon juice. Top evenly with salad.

5 **SmartPoints value per serving** (1 chicken breast and 2 cups salad): 347 Cal, 13 g Total Fat, 4 g Sat Fat, 671 mg Sod, 18 g Total Carb, 4 g Sugar, 3 g Fib, 38 g Prot.

**Chicken ratatouille
with penne**

Chicken ratatouille with penne

Serves 6

3   skinless boneless chicken breasts (about 1 pound)
2   teaspoons dried oregano
1   teaspoon salt
½   teaspoon black pepper
3   teaspoons olive oil
1   onion, chopped
3   garlic cloves, minced
½   cup dry white wine
½   pound eggplant, unpeeled, cut into 1-inch pieces
1   zucchini, cut into 1-inch pieces
1   yellow squash, cut into 1-inch pieces
1   red bell pepper, seeded and cut into 1-inch pieces
1   (28-ounce) can Italian peeled tomatoes, drained and chopped
6   ounces penne or ziti
½   cup chopped fresh basil
6   tablespoons shaved Parmesan

1 Sprinkle chicken with oregano, ½ teaspoon salt, and the pepper. Heat 1½ teaspoons oil in Dutch oven over medium-high heat. Add chicken to skillet and cook, turning occasionally, until chicken is cooked through, about 8 minutes. Transfer chicken to plate.

2 Add remaining 1½ teaspoons oil to Dutch oven. Add onion and garlic and cook, stirring often, until onion is softened, about 3 minutes. Add wine and cook, stirring constantly, until mixture comes to a boil and reduces slightly, about 3 minutes.

3 Add eggplant, zucchini, squash, bell pepper, tomatoes, and remaining ½ teaspoon salt; bring to boil. Reduce heat and simmer, covered, until vegetables are softened, about 15 minutes.

4 Meanwhile, cook penne according to package directions. Drain.

5 Cut chicken diagonally into thin slices. Add chicken to Dutch oven and cook until heated through, about 3 minutes. Stir in pasta and basil. Spoon evenly onto 6 plates and sprinkle each serving with 1 tablespoon Parmesan.

5 **SmartPoints value per serving** (1⅔ cups pasta mixture and 1 tablespoon cheese): 331 Cal, 7 g Total Fat, 2 g Sat Fat, 831 mg Sod, 39 g Total Carb, 10 g Sugar, 5 g Fib, 25 g Prot.

Let's do this together
Chicken breasts are one of WW member Kelly H.'s favorite ingredients for making crave-worthy meals she looks forward to eating. "I season them with a chipotle dry rub and use them in salads, marinate them for chicken and vegetable kebabs, or cook them in the slow cooker with salsa for tacos and burritos."

Creole jambalaya

Gluten Free   **Serves 6**

This traditional jambalaya starts with the "holy trinity" of New Orleans cooking: bell pepper, onion, and celery. It's a dish that Louisiana cooks created long ago to make an inexpensive meal that's filling and delicious. And it still is!

1   teaspoon canola oil

½   **pound fully cooked chicken andouille sausage, quartered lengthwise and sliced**

2   **red, orange, or yellow bell peppers, diced**

1   **onion, sliced**

2   **celery stalks, sliced**

3   **large garlic cloves, minced**

1   **cup long-grain white rice**

3   **cups chicken broth**

1   **(14½-ounce) can diced tomatoes, drained**

2   **teaspoons dried thyme**

¼   **teaspoon salt**

¼   **teaspoon cayenne**

¼   **teaspoon black pepper**

1   **bay leaf**

½   **pound large shrimp, peeled and deveined**

2   **tablespoons chopped fresh flat-leaf parsley**

1 Heat oil in large nonstick skillet over medium heat. Add sausage and cook, stirring occasionally, until sausage is browned, about 8 minutes. Add bell peppers, onion, celery, and garlic; cook, stirring occasionally, until vegetables are softened, about 10 minutes.

2 Stir in rice, broth, tomatoes, thyme, salt, cayenne, black pepper, and bay leaf; bring to boil. Reduce heat and simmer, covered, 25 minutes.

3 Stir in shrimp. Cook, covered, until shrimp are just opaque in center and rice is tender, about 5 minutes longer. Remove bay leaf and sprinkle with parsley.

5   **SmartPoints value per serving** (about 1⅓ cups): 252 Cal, 5 g Total Fat, 1 g Sat Fat, 1,044 mg Sod, 34 g Total Carb, 5 g Sugar, 3 g Fib, 17 g Prot.

Chicken and sausage paella

Gluten Free   **Serves 6**

Turkey kielbasa intensifies the flavor of this one-pan chicken-and-rice dinner. Saffron is traditionally used in paella, but if you don't have it on hand, don't let that keep you from making this weeknight meal with potential for leftovers.

4	**(5-ounce) skinless boneless chicken thighs, trimmed and cut into 3 pieces**
½	**teaspoon salt**
¼	**teaspoon black pepper**
2	**teaspoons olive oil**
4	**ounces turkey kielbasa or andouille sausage, cut into ¼-inch slices**
1	**onion, chopped**
1	**green bell pepper, chopped**
4	**garlic cloves, minced**
1½	**cups chicken broth**
1	**(14½-ounce) can petite diced tomatoes, drained**
¾	**cup long-grain white rice**
½	**cup frozen green peas**
8	**small pimiento-stuffed olives, sliced**
½	**teaspoon saffron threads, crushed**

1 Sprinkle chicken with salt and pepper. Heat oil in large skillet over medium-high heat. Add chicken and cook, turning once, until chicken is browned, about 8 minutes. Transfer to plate.

2 Add kielbasa to skillet and cook 1 minute, stirring often, until kielbasa is browned; transfer to plate with chicken. Add onion, bell pepper, and garlic to skillet; cook, stirring with wooden spoon to scrape up browned bits from bottom of pan, until vegetables begin to soften, 2–3 minutes. Add chicken, kielbasa, broth, tomatoes, rice, peas, olives, and saffron and bring to boil. Reduce heat, cover, and simmer until rice is tender and liquid is absorbed, 20 minutes. Remove from heat and let stand 10 minutes before serving.

6 **SmartPoints value per serving** (generous ¾ cup rice mixture and 2 chicken pieces): 297 Cal, 9 g Total Fat, 2 g Sat Fat, 842 mg Sod, 27 g Total Carb, 4 g Sugar, 3 g Fib, 26 g Prot.

Freestyle it
Make a colorful and crunchy 0 SmartPoints salad to serve with the paella. Toss up romaine, radicchio, water-packed roasted red bell peppers, cherry tomatoes, cucumbers, red-wine vinegar, salt, and pepper in a big salad bowl.

Chicken, caramelized onion, and goat cheese pizza

Serves 6

1	**tablespoon olive oil**
3	**large onions, thinly sliced**
3	**garlic cloves, minced**
1	**teaspoon minced fresh rosemary**
1½	**tablespoons balsamic vinegar**
2	**cups diced cooked or grilled skinless chicken breast**
10	**Kalamata olives, pitted and thinly sliced**
½	**teaspoon salt**
¼	**teaspoon black pepper**
1	**(10-ounce) prebaked thin pizza crust**
⅔	**cup crumbled reduced-fat goat cheese**
2	**tablespoons chopped fresh flat-leaf parsley**

1 Preheat oven to 450°F. Spray large baking sheet with nonstick spray.

2 Heat oil in large skillet over medium-high heat. Add onions; cook, covered, stirring occasionally, until onions are deep golden, about 30 minutes. Stir in garlic and rosemary; cook, stirring frequently, until fragrant, about 30 seconds. Stir in vinegar. Remove pan from heat and stir in chicken, olives, salt, and pepper.

3 Top crust evenly with chicken mixture; sprinkle evenly with goat cheese. Bake until cheese softens and crust is crisp, 8–10 minutes. Sprinkle with parsley and cut into 6 wedges.

(7) **SmartPoints value per serving** (1 wedge): 336 Cal, 10 g Total Fat, 3 g Sat Fat, 641 mg Sod, 37 g Total Carb, 3 g Sugar, 2 g Fib, 23 g Prot.

Let's do this together

"My favorite shortcut is my slow cooker," says WW member Jordon Hamel. "I throw chicken breast in, cook it, and then shred or chop it for dishes like casseroles, tacos, and soups." We think this chicken pizza is a great use, too.

Chicken, caramelized onion, and goat cheese pizza

Stovetop cassoulet

Stovetop cassoulet

Gluten Free   **Serves 8**

1   pound skinless boneless chicken thighs, trimmed and cut into 2-inch chunks

½   teaspoon salt

¼   teaspoon black pepper

2   teaspoons olive oil

½   pound turkey kielbasa or turkey andouille, sliced

2   carrots, chopped

1   Granny Smith apple, peeled, cored, and chopped

1   leek (white and pale green parts only), chopped

3   garlic cloves, minced

2   (15½-ounce) cans cannellini (white kidney) beans, rinsed and drained

1   (14½-ounce) can diced tomatoes

2   cups chicken broth

¼   cup dry white wine

⅛   teaspoon ground allspice

1   bay leaf

2   tablespoons chopped fresh flat-leaf parsley

1   tablespoon grated lemon zest

1 Sprinkle chicken with salt and pepper. Heat 1 teaspoon oil in Dutch oven over medium-high heat. Add chicken and cook, turning occasionally, until chicken is no longer pink, about 5 minutes; transfer chicken and juices to medium bowl. Add remaining 1 teaspoon oil and kielbasa to Dutch oven. Cook, stirring occasionally, until kielbasa is browned, about 4 minutes.

2 Add carrots, apple, leek, and two-thirds of garlic to Dutch oven. Cook, stirring occasionally, about 2 minutes. Return chicken and juices to Dutch oven along with beans, tomatoes, broth, wine, allspice, and bay leaf; bring to boil. Reduce heat and simmer, covered, until chicken is cooked through and vegetables are tender, about 25 minutes.

3 Mix together parsley, lemon zest, and remaining garlic in small cup; set aside.

4 Discard bay leaf; sprinkle cassoulet with parsley mixture just before serving.

3 **SmartPoints value per serving** (generous 1 cup): 256 Cal, 6 g Total Fat, 2 g Sat Fat, 1,080 mg Sod, 25 g Total Carb, 5 g Sugar, 5 g Fib, 23 g Prot.

Let's do this together

This big-batch recipe is the kind of dish WW member Sheri Friedman likes to make. "When scheduling the week's meals, I plan out the dinners and work backward from there," she explains. "Many times, the leftovers from dinner are part of my lunch. I love a meal that keeps on giving!"

Wild mushroom and sausage risotto

Gluten Free   Serves 6

To add a bit of freshness and some more veggies to the risotto, stir in a few handfuls of baby spinach during the last minute of cooking time.

1   **(32-ounce) carton chicken broth**

2   **teaspoons olive oil**

½   **pound sun-dried tomato or roasted red pepper chicken sausage, casings removed, diced**

1   **onion, finely chopped**

1   **large garlic clove, minced**

1   **(4-ounce) package sliced mixed wild mushrooms**

2   **teaspoons chopped fresh thyme**

1   **cup Arborio rice**

⅓   **cup dry white wine**

4   **tablespoons grated Parmesan**

¼   **teaspoon black pepper**

1 Bring broth to boil in medium saucepan. Reduce heat and keep at simmer.

2 Meanwhile, heat oil in large saucepan over medium-high heat. Add sausage, onion, and garlic and cook, stirring occasionally, until lightly browned, 8–9 minutes. Add mushrooms and thyme. Cook, stirring occasionally, until mushrooms begin to soften, about 2 minutes. Stir in rice; reduce heat to medium and cook, stirring constantly, 1 minute. Add wine and cook, stirring constantly, until liquid is absorbed, about 1 minute.

3 Add broth, ½ cup at a time, stirring until broth is absorbed before adding more. Cook just until rice is tender, 18–20 minutes (you may have up to a cup of broth left over). Remove saucepan from heat and stir in 2 tablespoons Parmesan and the pepper. Spoon risotto evenly into 4 shallow bowls and sprinkle evenly with remaining 2 tablespoons Parmesan. Serve at once.

 SmartPoints value per serving (⅔ cup risotto and 1 teaspoon Parmesan): 263 Cal, 7 g Total Fat, 2 g Sat Fat, 761 mg Sod, 31 g Total Carb, 3 g Sugar, 2 g Fib, 14 g Prot.

Let's do this together
Planning meals for the week is essential to success for WW member René Falgout. "Typically our family is very busy, and if I don't have meals planned out, I'm more apt to drive through that fast-food line to save time," she says. "Planning meals ahead takes away the fast-food excuse."

Wild mushroom and
sausage risotto

Chicken, corn, and black bean pizza

Serves 6

1	**lime**
2	**cups diced cooked skinless chicken breast**
½	**cup shredded pepper Jack**
¼	**cup crumbled cotija cheese**
2	**scallions, thinly sliced**
1	**(10-ounce) prebaked thin pizza crust**
¾	**cup enchilada sauce**
⅔	**cup canned black beans, rinsed and drained**
½	**avocado, pitted and diced**
¼	**cup chopped fresh cilantro**

1 Preheat oven to 450°F. Spray large baking sheet with nonstick spray.

2 Grate zest from lime; cut lime into wedges. Combine chicken and lime zest in medium bowl and toss to coat. Combine pepper Jack, cotija, and scallions in another medium bowl and toss to combine.

3 Lightly spray crust with nonstick spray. Place crust on baking sheet and bake until crisp, 5 minutes.

4 Spread hot crust with ½ cup enchilada sauce. Top evenly with chicken and beans; drizzle with remaining ¼ cup sauce. Sprinkle evenly with cheese mixture. Bake until cheeses begin to melt, about 5 minutes longer. Sprinkle with avocado and cilantro. Cut pizza into 6 wedges and serve immediately with lime wedges.

 9 **SmartPoints value per serving** (1 wedge): 382 Cal, 13 g Total Fat, 5 g Sat Fat, 680 mg Sod, 38 g Total Carb, 1 g Sugar, 4 g Fib, 26 g Prot.

Cook's tip

As this recipe shows, pizza doesn't have to be Italian. Spread the crust with marinara, tomato, taco, enchilada, or barbecue sauce, then top with tender, quick-cooking vegetables, canned beans, and cooked chicken or turkey. As for the cheese, anything goes.

Turkey mushroom-barley soup with dill

Serves 6

We almost always add garlic after cooking other vegetables for a few minutes. This allows the veggies to give off some moisture to help prevent the garlic from burning.

1 **tablespoon olive oil**

2 **carrots, sliced**

2 **celery stalks with leaves, chopped**

1 **onion, chopped**

½ **pound cremini mushrooms, thickly sliced**

2 **garlic cloves, minced**

1 **(48-ounce) carton chicken broth**

¼ **teaspoon black pepper**

Pinch cayenne

½ **cup quick-cooking barley**

2 **cups diced cooked skinless turkey or chicken breast**

¼ **cup snipped fresh dill**

Lemon wedges

1 Heat oil in Dutch oven over medium heat. Add carrots, celery, and onion; cook, stirring, until onion is softened, about 5 minutes. Add mushrooms and cook, stirring occasionally, until mushrooms are softened, about 4 minutes. Stir in garlic and cook, stirring constantly, until fragrant, about 30 seconds.

2 Add broth, black pepper, and cayenne to pot; bring to boil. Stir in barley and return to boil. Reduce heat and simmer, covered, until barley is tender, about 10 minutes. Stir in turkey and simmer just until heated through, about 2 minutes longer. Ladle evenly into 6 bowls and sprinkle evenly with dill. Serve with lemon wedges.

2   **SmartPoints value per serving** (about 1⅓ cups): 177 Cal, 6 g Total Fat, 1 g Sat Fat, 748 mg Sod, 10 g Total Carb, 3 g Sugar, 2 g Fib, 21 g Prot.

Let's do this together

WW member Kam Szabo shares with us that she uses rotisserie chicken to make a phenomenal chicken soup. We think that's a great use for supermarket rotisserie chicken.

**Chicken pot pie with
chive biscuits**

Chicken pot pie with chive biscuits

Serves 6

2	**teaspoons butter**
2	**shallots, finely chopped**
1	**pound assorted fresh mushrooms, sliced (such as white, cremini, oyster, and shiitake)**
3	**carrots, sliced**
½	**cup dry white wine**
¼	**cup all-purpose flour**
2	**cups chicken broth**
1	**pound cooked skinless chicken breast, shredded**
1	**cup thawed frozen green peas**
¼	**cup plus ⅓ cup fat-free half-and-half**
1	**teaspoon chopped fresh thyme**
¾	**teaspoon salt**
⅛	**teaspoon cayenne**
1	**cup reduced-fat pancake and baking mix**
2	**tablespoons minced fresh chives**

1 Preheat oven to 400°F. Spray shallow 2½-quart baking dish with nonstick spray.

2 To make filling, melt butter in large skillet over medium heat. Add shallots and cook, stirring often, until golden, 2–3 minutes. Add mushrooms and carrots; increase heat to medium-high and cook, stirring occasionally, until mushrooms are tender, 5 minutes. Add wine and increase heat to high; boil, stirring occasionally, until evaporated, 8–9 minutes. Stir in flour until blended.

3 Gradually stir in broth; bring to boil. Reduce heat to low; simmer, stirring with wooden spoon to scrape up browned bits from bottom of skillet, 1 minute. Stir in chicken, peas, ¼ cup half-and-half, the thyme, salt, and cayenne. Spoon into prepared baking dish.

4 To make topping, stir together pancake mix, remaining ⅓ cup half-and-half, and the chives. Drop by heaping tablespoonsful over filling to form 12 biscuits.

5 Bake until biscuits are golden brown and filling is bubbly, 18–20 minutes

5 **SmartPoints value per serving** (1 cup filling and 2 biscuits): 321 Cal, 6 g Total Fat, 2 g Sat Fat, 1,146 mg Sod, 36 g Total Carb, 9 g Sugar, 4 g Fib, 30 g Prot.

Let's do this together
Cooking chicken breasts in bulk ahead of time is a big time-saver for WW member Brianna Engebretsen. "You can use it to make burrito bowls, turn it into BBQ chicken sandwiches, or make chicken salad," she explains. "The possibilities are endless with cooked chicken."

Ginger meatball and vegetable soup

Gluten Free   Serves 6

These gingery meatballs are a snap to make—you just drop them from a tablespoon onto the broiler rack. While the meatballs cook, the veggies simmer, so it's a one-pot meal that tastes like it took much longer to make.

1	**pound ground skinless turkey breast**
1	**shallot, minced**
1	**large egg white**
4	**teaspoons fresh grated peeled ginger**
¼	**cup chopped fresh cilantro**
¼	**teaspoon salt, or to taste**
¼	**teaspoon black pepper**
6	**cups chicken broth**
1	**teaspoon chili-garlic sauce**
4	**cups shredded Napa cabbage**
2	**carrots, cut into thin strips**
1	**small red bell pepper, cut into thin strips**
1	**tablespoon lime juice**
1	**tablespoon Asian fish sauce**
2	**scallions, thinly sliced**

1 Spray broiler rack with nonstick spray. Preheat broiler.

2 Stir together turkey, shallot, egg white, 2 teaspoons ginger, the cilantro, salt, and pepper in large bowl. Drop mixture by tablespoonfuls onto prepared broiler rack. Broil 5 inches from heat, turning once, until cooked through, about 8 minutes. Set aside.

3 Meanwhile, combine broth, chili-garlic sauce, and remaining 2 teaspoons ginger in Dutch oven. Bring to boil over medium-high heat. Add cabbage, carrots, and bell pepper and return to boil. Reduce heat to medium-low and simmer until vegetables are crisp-tender, about 5 minutes. Remove from heat and gently stir in meatballs, lime juice, and fish sauce.

4 Ladle evenly into 6 bowls and sprinkle with scallions.

1 **SmartPoints value per serving** (about 1½ cups): 160 Cal, 3 g Total Fat, 1 g Sat Fat, 1,167 mg Sod, 8 g Total Carb, 4 g Sugar, 2 g Fib, 24 g Prot.

Cook's tip

If you want to add noodles to the soup, cook 3 ounces of thin rice noodles according to package directions and stir in just before serving. The per-serving SmartPoints will increase by 2.

Ginger meatball and vegetable soup

**Very veggie turkey
meat loaf**

Very veggie turkey meat loaf

Serves 6

Ground turkey breast can be dry when it's used in meat loaf or turkey burgers, but adding fresh vegetables increases the moisture. To make your ground turkey recipes a little juicier, try the trick we used in this recipe: Add some shredded zucchini or carrot.

1	teaspoon olive oil
½	small onion, finely chopped
2	carrots, coarsely shredded
1	(5-ounce) package baby spinach
1	zucchini, coarsely shredded
3	garlic cloves, minced
2	teaspoons minced fresh rosemary
1	large egg
2	tablespoons Dijon mustard
2	tablespoons Worcestershire sauce
½	teaspoon salt
¼	teaspoon black pepper
1	pound ground skinless turkey breast
1	cup uncooked quick or old-fashioned oats
½	cup shredded part-skim mozzarella

1 Preheat oven to 375°F. Line large rimmed baking sheet with foil; spray foil with nonstick spray.

2 Heat oil in large skillet over medium-high heat. Add onion and cook, stirring often, until onion begins to soften, about 3 minutes. Add carrots, spinach, zucchini, garlic, and rosemary. Cover and cook, stirring occasionally, until vegetables soften, about 3 minutes. Drain and transfer to large shallow dish to cool slightly.

3 Whisk together egg, mustard, Worcestershire sauce, salt, and pepper in large bowl. Add turkey, oats, and vegetable mixture and stir to mix well.

4 Transfer mixture to baking pan and form into 4 x 10-inch loaf. Bake until instant-read thermometer inserted into center of meat loaf registers 165°F, about 50 minutes. Sprinkle with mozzarella and let stand 5 minutes before cutting into 12 slices.

3 **SmartPoints value per serving** (2 slices): 212 Cal, 6 g Total Fat, 2 g Sat Fat, 510 mg Sod, 15 g Total Carb, 3 g Sugar, 3 g Fib, 24 g Prot.

Let's do this together

For WW member Kathy Petrullo, one of the keys to being successful is learning how to cook the foods she loves—like meat loaf and lasagna—in the healthiest way possible. "People who eat my versions of these foods enjoy them without realizing they are Weight Watchers–friendly!"

Turkey, spinach, and goat cheese enchiladas

Serves 4

This recipe uses corn and wheat–blend tortillas. They're a cross between corn tortillas and flour tortillas and have a unique flavor. If you can't find them, just use ordinary flour tortillas in this recipe.

2	**teaspoons olive oil**
1	**pound ground skinless turkey breast**
2	**garlic cloves, minced**
½	**teaspoon ground cumin**
½	**teaspoon black pepper**
¼	**teaspoon salt**
1	**(9-ounce) bag fresh spinach**
3	**ounces reduced-fat goat cheese, crumbled**
1	**(16-ounce) jar tomatillo salsa**
8	**(6-inch) corn and wheat–blend tortillas (such as Mission)**
2	**scallions, thinly sliced**
¼	**cup fresh cilantro leaves**
Lime wedges	

1 Preheat oven to 350°F. Spray 9 x 13-inch baking dish with nonstick spray.

2 Heat oil in large nonstick skillet over medium heat. Add turkey, garlic, cumin, pepper, and salt and cook, breaking it apart with wooden spoon, until turkey is no longer pink, about 3 minutes. Add spinach in batches and cook, tossing with tongs, just until spinach is wilted, about 3 minutes. Remove from heat and stir in goat cheese.

3 Pour half of salsa into prepared baking dish. Working with one tortilla at a time, spoon about 3 tablespoons filling down center of each tortilla. Roll up and place seam side down into baking dish. Pour remaining salsa over enchiladas. Bake until hot, about 20 minutes. Sprinkle with scallions and cilantro and serve with lime wedges.

 SmartPoints value per serving (2 enchiladas): 446 Cal, 14 g Total Fat, 4 g Sat Fat, 1,156 mg Sod, 44 g Total Carb, 4 g Sugar, 12 g Fib, 37 g Prot.

Let's do this together
WW member Thomas Halloran does his grocery shopping with focus. "I do not roam the aisles and I definitely do not go to the store hungry," he tells us. "I make a list and I know exactly what ingredients I need, and I do not waiver from the list."

Turkey, spinach, and
goat cheese enchiladas

Turkey, spinach, and mushroom lasagna

Serves 12

Made with purchased marinara sauce and no-boil noodles, this veggie-packed lasagna cuts a few corners without sacrificing flavor. Invite guests and enjoy it for weekend entertaining, or make it with leftovers in mind for later in the week.

3	**teaspoons olive oil**
1	**pound ground turkey (7% fat or less)**
¾	**teaspoon salt**
¼	**teaspoon black pepper**
1	**small onion, chopped**
1	**(10-ounce) package cremini mushrooms, sliced**
2	**large garlic cloves, minced**
1	**pound baby spinach**
4	**cups good-quality marinara sauce**
1	**(8-ounce) box no-boil lasagna noodles (12 noodles)**
1	**(16-ounce) container part-skim ricotta**
1½	**cups shredded part-skim mozzarella**

1 Preheat oven to 375°F. Spray 9 x 13-inch baking dish with nonstick spray.

2 Heat 1 teaspoon oil in large nonstick skillet over medium heat. Add turkey, ½ teaspoon salt, and the pepper and cook, stirring frequently, until turkey is no longer pink, about 5 minutes. Transfer to large bowl.

3 Add remaining 2 teaspoons oil to skillet. Add onion and remaining ¼ teaspoon salt and cook, stirring often, until onion is lightly browned, about 4 minutes. Add mushrooms and garlic; cook, stirring often, until mushrooms are softened, about 5 minutes. Add spinach in batches and cook, stirring often, until spinach is wilted, about 6 minutes longer. Add mushroom mixture to turkey, stirring to combine.

4 To assemble, spread 1 cup marinara sauce over bottom of prepared baking dish. Cover with 4 lasagna noodles, overlapping them, if needed. Cover with half of turkey mixture, dot with half of ricotta, and top with 1 cup marinara sauce. Add another layer of 4 noodles; cover with remaining turkey mixture, remaining ricotta, 1 cup marinara sauce, and remaining 4 noodles. Spread remaining 1 cup marinara sauce on top and sprinkle with mozzarella.

5 Spray sheet of foil with nonstick spray; cover dish with foil, sprayed side down, and bake 30 minutes. Remove foil and bake until mozzarella is slightly browned and noodles are very tender, about 20 minutes longer. Let cool 15 minutes before cutting into 12 pieces.

8 **SmartPoints value per serving** (¹⁄₁₂ of lasagna): 289 Cal, 12 g Total Fat, 5 g Sat Fat, 671 mg Sod, 26 g Total Carb, 5 g Sugar, 4 g Fib, 20 g Prot.

Rigatoni with turkey bolognese

Serves 4

Classic Bolognese sauce made with turkey breast instead of beef makes this family favorite SmartPoints-friendlier. Don't mention that it's made with turkey—they probably won't even notice!

2	**teaspoons olive oil**
1	**onion, chopped**
1	**celery stalk, chopped**
1	**carrot, chopped**
1	**large garlic clove, minced**
½	**pound ground skinless turkey breast**
½	**teaspoon salt**
¼	**teaspoon black pepper**
1	**(28-ounce) can Italian-style whole tomatoes**
¼	**cup finely chopped fresh parsley**
¼	**cup dry red wine or beef broth**
1	**fresh rosemary sprig**
1	**bay leaf**
2	**cups rigatoni**
¼	**cup grated Parmesan**

1 Heat oil in Dutch oven over medium-high heat. Add onion and cook, stirring frequently, until onion is softened, about 5 minutes. Add celery, carrot, and garlic; cover and cook, stirring occasionally, until vegetables are softened, about 5 minutes.

2 Add turkey, salt, and pepper and cook, breaking it apart with wooden spoon, until turkey is browned, about 5 minutes. Stir in tomatoes, parsley, wine, rosemary, and bay leaf. Cook, stirring with wooden spoon to break apart tomatoes, until mixture comes to boil. Reduce heat and simmer, stirring occasionally, until thickened, about 45 minutes. Discard rosemary and bay leaf.

3 Meanwhile, cook rigatoni according to package directions. Transfer to serving bowl. Add sauce and toss. Sprinkle with Parmesan.

6 **SmartPoints value per serving** (1½ cups): 328 Cal, 6 g Total Fat, 2 g Sat Fat, 838 mg Sod, 42 g Total Carb, 8 g Sugar, 4 g Fib, 22 g Prot.

Cook's tip
Why not treat yourself to a glass of wine with this dish—the bottle is already open from making the sauce! A 5-ounce glass of wine will add 4 SmartPoints to your meal.

Greek turkey
meatballs

Greek turkey meatballs

Serves 6

Carry through on the Greek theme of this recipe and serve the meatballs and sauce over orzo (½ cup cooked orzo per serving will increase the SmartPoints by 3).

¾ **pound ground skinless turkey breast**

1 **onion, chopped**

⅓ **cup plain dried bread crumbs**

1 **large egg**

¼ **cup grated pecorino Romano**

4 **garlic cloves, minced**

3 **tablespoons chopped fresh flat-leaf parsley, plus additional for garnish**

1 **tablespoon chopped fresh mint, plus additional for garnish**

2 **teaspoons dried oregano**

1 **teaspoon salt**

¼ **teaspoon black pepper**

½ **teaspoon cinnamon**

1 **tablespoon olive oil**

1 **(28-ounce) can diced tomatoes**

3 **tablespoons tomato paste**

1 Preheat oven to 400°F. Spray large rimmed baking sheet with nonstick spray.

2 To prepare meatballs, stir together turkey, ½ cup onion, the bread crumbs, egg, pecorino Romano, half of garlic, 3 tablespoons parsley, 1 tablespoon mint, 1 teaspoon oregano, ½ teaspoon salt, the pepper, and ¼ teaspoon cinnamon in large bowl just until mixed. With damp hands, form into 18 (1-inch) meatballs. Place meatballs on prepared baking sheet and bake, turning once, 20 minutes.

3 Meanwhile, heat oil in Dutch oven over medium-high heat. Add remaining onion, remaining garlic, and remaining 1 teaspoon oregano. Cook, stirring often, until onion is softened, about 3 minutes. Stir in tomatoes with their juice, tomato paste, remaining ½ teaspoon salt, and remaining ¼ teaspoon cinnamon; bring to boil. Reduce heat to low and cook, stirring occasionally, until sauce is slightly thickened, about 15 minutes. Add meatballs and simmer about 15 minutes longer. Remove from heat and sprinkle with additional parsley and mint.

 SmartPoints value per serving (3 meatballs and about ½ cup sauce): 184 Cal, 7 g Total Fat, 2 g Sat Fat, 796 mg Sod, 14 g Total Carb, 5 g Sugar, 3 g Fib, 17 g Prot.

Let's do this together

A kitchen tip that saves a tremendous amount of time comes from WW member Kshatriya Millick: "I've spent a lot of time decluttering and organizing my space," Kshatriya says. "Everything I need to cook with is just an arm's length away, and I can move from one task to another with speed and ease."

Chapter 6

Sunday roasts

Roast chicken with prosciutto stuffing, 180
Sweet-and-smoky roast chicken, 182
Carving 101, 183
Roast chicken and vegetables Provençal, 185
Roast chicken with meyer lemons and shallot sauce, 186
Roast chicken with artichokes and potatoes, 189
Red curry roast chicken with coconut sauce, 190
Butterflied roast chicken with herbed potatoes, 191
Roast capon with bourbon sauce, 192
Roast capon with pomegranate glaze, 194
Roast capon with orange and root veggies, 195
Herbed cornish hens under a brick, 197
Maple-glazed cornish hens with spinach and pear, 198
Fennel-spiced roast turkey with mushroom gravy, 199
Honey herb roast turkey breast with pan gravy, 200
Turkey breast with apples, fennel, and barley, 201
Leek and herb–stuffed bacon-wrapped turkey, 203

Roast chicken with prosciutto stuffing

Serves 6

In this recipe, you put the chicken in the oven, then make the stuffing and bake it at the same time. The prosciutto and tarragon give an updated twist to a home-style meal that's company-worthy.

Stuffing

4	cups (1-inch) bread cubes (about 4 ounces)
2	teaspoons olive oil
1	large onion, quartered and thinly sliced
1	celery stalk, chopped
2	slices prosciutto, chopped
3	tablespoons chopped fresh parsley
2	tablespoons chopped fresh tarragon
1	large egg, lightly beaten
⅓	cup chicken broth
½	teaspoon grated lemon zest
¼	teaspoon salt
¼	teaspoon black pepper

Chicken

1	(3½-pound) whole chicken, giblets discarded
½	teaspoon salt
½	teaspoon black pepper
1	small lemon, halved
1	small onion, quartered
3	fresh tarragon sprigs

1 Preheat oven to 375°F.

2 Place bread cubes on large baking sheet and spread in single layer. Bake, stirring once, until lightly toasted, about 8 minutes. Transfer to large bowl. Set aside. Maintain oven temperature.

3 To make chicken, spray medium roasting pan with nonstick spray. Place chicken in pan. With your fingers, loosen skin on chicken breasts, legs, and thighs. Rub salt and pepper on meat under skin; press skin back into place. Place lemon halves, onion quarters, and tarragon sprigs inside cavity of chicken. Tuck wings under chicken and tie legs together with kitchen string. Roast until instant-read thermometer inserted into thigh registers 165°F, about 1 hour and 15 minutes.

4 Meanwhile, to make stuffing, spray 1½-quart baking dish with nonstick spray.

5 Heat oil in large skillet. Add onion and celery and cook, stirring often, until vegetables are softened and lightly browned, about 8 minutes. Add onion mixture, prosciutto, parsley, tarragon, egg, chicken broth, lemon zest, salt, and pepper to bread cubes and toss to combine. Spoon mixture into prepared baking dish; cover and bake 20 minutes. Uncover and bake until top is lightly browned, about 15 minutes longer.

6 Remove chicken from oven and transfer to carving board. Let stand 10 minutes before carving. Discard skin before eating.

 SmartPoints value per serving (⅙ of chicken and about ⅔ cup stuffing): 277 Cal, 8 g Total Fat, 2 g Sat Fat, 610 mg Sod, 15 g Total Carb, 3 g Sugar, 2 g Fib, 33 g Prot.

Roast chicken with prosciutto stuffing

Sweet-and-smoky roast chicken

Gluten Free   Serves 6

Smoked paprika, which gives this chicken its flame-kissed flavor, is made from sweet red peppers that are smoked and dried. It's not spicy, but the smoky flavor is bold, so use it sparingly.

2	**tablespoons packed brown sugar**
4	**teaspoons smoked paprika**
4	**teaspoons balsamic vinegar**
1	**tablespoon Sriracha**
2	**large garlic cloves, crushed through a press**
¾	**teaspoon salt**
1	**(3½-pound) whole chicken, giblets removed**

1 Preheat oven to 375°F. Spray roasting rack with nonstick spray and place in roasting pan.

2 Combine brown sugar, paprika, vinegar, Sriracha, garlic, and salt in small bowl. With your fingers, loosen skin on chicken breasts, legs, and thighs. Rub seasoning mixture on meat under skin; press skin back into place. Tuck wings under chicken and tie legs together with kitchen string. Place chicken on rack in roasting pan, breast side up. Roast until instant-read thermometer inserted into thigh registers 165°F, 1¼–1½ hours.

3 Transfer chicken to cutting board; let stand 10 minutes. Meanwhile, pour pan juices into glass measuring cup; skim and discard fat.

4 Discard skin and wings and carve chicken into 6 pieces. Serve with pan juices.

4 **SmartPoints value per serving** (1 piece chicken and 2 teaspoons pan juices): 184 Cal, 4 g Total Fat, 1 g Sat Fat, 325 mg Sod, 6 g Total Carb, 5 g Sugar, 1 g Fib, 28 g Prot.

Let's do this together
WW member Dr. Ronald E. Hunter Jr. is a fan of recipes like this one. "Anything I can pop into the oven, such as baked chicken, is a go-to dish," he explains. "While it cooks, I put rice in the rice cooker, then I pop a bag of steamed veggies into the microwave and then the whole meal is done."

Carving 101

Carving a whole bird? It's a lot easier than you think. These instructions work for a chicken or turkey. It's a straightforward task, but you might want to practice your technique on a chicken before tackling the job on a holiday turkey as your guests watch. (Still nervous? Present the whole roasted bird to your guests for oooohs and ahhhs, then take it back to the kitchen and carve it in private.)

1   Place your roasted chicken or turkey, breast side up, on a carving board and allow it to rest (10 minutes for a chicken, 30 minutes for a turkey). Have ready a sharp boning or carving knife, carving fork, and a platter to hold the carved pieces.

2   Loosen the leg on one side by cutting through the skin between the thigh and breast. Cut down until you reach the thigh joint. Grab the tip of the leg and bend it outward until you see where the joint connects to the carcass; cut through the joint, removing the whole leg. Repeat on the other side.

3   Place one leg at a time, skin side down, and find the joint that connects the thigh to the drumstick. Cut down through the joint to separate the drumstick and thigh. Slice the thigh meat away from the bone, if desired.

4   Pull a wing away from the body so you can see where it is attached below the breast. Find the joint with the tip of your knife and cut through the joint. Repeat on the other side.

5   To remove the breast meat, feel for the breast bone at the top of the bird. Starting with the tip of the knife, cut down along one side of the breast bone. Angling your knife slightly, slice down along the rib cage to remove the meat in one piece. Repeat on the other side.

6   Serve the breasts whole or cut them into thin slices at an angle. Arrange all the pieces on your platter. If you like, you can garnish the platter with fresh herbs, citrus wedges, or roasted onions or potatoes.

Roast chicken and vegetables Provençal

Roast chicken and vegetables Provençal

Gluten Free   Serves 6

In this one-pan recipe, you roast an herbed whole chicken with a garden of vegetables—plus some Kalamata olives thrown in to put the flavor over the top. Pull out your largest baking sheet for this one.

4	**garlic cloves, minced**
1	**tablespoon chopped fresh rosemary**
1	**tablespoon chopped fresh thyme**
1	**tablespoon chopped fresh tarragon**
1	**tablespoon olive oil**
¾	**teaspoon salt**
½	**teaspoon black pepper**
1	**(3½-pound) whole chicken, giblets removed**
1	**small lemon, quartered**
1	**pound small red potatoes**
2	**red onions, each cut into 6 wedges**
3	**plum tomatoes, halved**
½	**teaspoon dried oregano**
1	**zucchini, cut into 1½-inch chunks**
1	**yellow squash, cut into 1½-inch chunks**
10	**Kalamata olives, pitted and chopped**
2	**tablespoons chopped fresh parsley**

1 Preheat oven to 425°F. Spray large rimmed baking sheet with nonstick spray.

2 Stir together 1 garlic clove, the rosemary, thyme, tarragon, oil, ½ teaspoon salt, and ¼ teaspoon pepper in small bowl.

3 With your fingers, loosen skin on chicken breasts, legs, and thighs. Rub garlic mixture evenly on meat under skin; press skin back into place. Place lemon in cavity of chicken, then tuck wings under chicken and tie legs with kitchen string. Place chicken in pan, breast side up.

4 Combine potatoes, onions, tomatoes, oregano, remaining ¼ teaspoon salt, and remaining ¼ teaspoon pepper in large bowl. Spray vegetables lightly with olive oil nonstick spray. Arrange vegetables around chicken. Roast, stirring vegetables occasionally, about 45 minutes. Add zucchini, squash, olives, and remaining 3 garlic cloves, to vegetables in pan and toss well. Continue roasting until an instant-read thermometer inserted into thigh registers 165°F and vegetables are tender, about 25 minutes longer.

5 Transfer chicken to a cutting board; let rest 10 minutes. Remove skin, then carve. Stir parsley into vegetables; serve chicken with vegetables.

⑤ SmartPoints value per serving (⅙ of chicken and vegetables): 278 Cal, 7 g Total Fat, 1 g Sat Fat, 359 mg Sod, 22 g Total Carb, 6 g Sugar, 4 g Fib, 31 g Prot.

Let's do this together

If you have leftover chicken from this recipe, it's great for a meal the next day. WW member René Falgout uses leftover chicken to make a chicken salad sandwich for lunch, or to add to fried rice or a pasta dish.

Roast chicken with meyer lemons and shallot sauce

Gluten Free   Serves 6

Roasted shallots are used to make an incredibly simple yet amazingly delicious sauce for a whole chicken. Serve the carved chicken and sauce on top of tender greens such as baby arugula, kale, or spinach.

1	**(3½-pound) chicken, giblets removed**
¾	**teaspoon salt**
½	**teaspoon black pepper**
3	**small meyer or regular lemons, halved crosswise**
4	**small shallots, peeled**
¾	**cup chicken broth**
1	**tablespoon chopped fresh parsley**

1 Preheat oven to 400°F. Spray medium roasting pan with nonstick spray.

2 Sprinkle chicken with ½ teaspoon salt and ¼ teaspoon pepper. Tuck wings under chicken and tie legs together with kitchen string. Place chicken in roasting pan, breast side up. Place lemon halves in roasting pan, cut side down. Scatter shallots around chicken.

3 Roast chicken 30 minutes; add broth to pan. Continue roasting until instant-read thermometer inserted into thigh registers 165°F, about 30 minutes longer. Transfer chicken to cutting board and let stand 10 minutes.

4 To make sauce, when cool enough to handle, coarsely chop shallots. Transfer shallots to mini–food processor. Skim off fat from pan juices. Add pan juices and remaining ¼ teaspoon salt and remaining ¼ teaspoon pepper to food processor; pulse until sauce is smooth.

5 Carve chicken and divide among 6 plates. Sprinkle with parsley. Serve with sauce and lemon halves. Remove skin before eating.

 3 **SmartPoints value per serving** (⅙ of chicken, 1 lemon half, and 2 tablespoons sauce): 187 Cal, 4 g Total Fat, 1 g Sat Fat, 387 mg Sod, 6 g Total Carb, 2 g Sugar, 2 g Fib, 29 g Prot.

Cook's tip
Meyer lemons are a cross between a mandarin orange and a lemon. They have smooth canary yellow skin and are less acidic than regular lemons. If you can't find them, this chicken dish will still be delicious using standard supermarket lemons.

Roast chicken with meyer lemons and shallot sauce

Roast chicken
with artichokes
and potatoes

Roast chicken with artichokes and potatoes

Gluten Free   Serves 6

A flavorful celebration of spring, this one-pan meal has a lemon-and-thyme–seasoned chicken with fingerling potatoes and artichokes scattered alongside.

2	**garlic cloves, minced**
2	**teaspoons minced fresh thyme**
3	**teaspoons grated lemon zest**
1	**teaspoon olive oil**
¾	**teaspoon salt**
½	**teaspoon black pepper**
1	**(3½-pound) whole chicken, giblets removed**
1½	**pounds fingerling or baby potatoes, halved or quartered if large**
4	**tablespoons lemon juice**
1	**cup water**
1	**pound baby artichokes**

1 Preheat oven to 400°F.

2 Combine garlic, thyme, 1 teaspoon lemon zest, the oil, ½ teaspoon salt, and the pepper in small bowl.

3 With your fingers, loosen skin on chicken breasts, legs, and thighs. Rub half of garlic mixture on meat under skin; press skin back into place. Place chicken in large roasting pan. If desired, tuck wings under chicken and tie legs together with kitchen string.

4 Combine potatoes and remaining garlic mixture in medium bowl and toss to coat. Arrange potatoes around chicken.

5 Combine 2 tablespoons lemon juice and ½ cup of water in large bowl. Pull tough outer leaves from artichokes and trim stem. Cut off about ½ inch from tip of each artichoke. Cut each artichoke in half lengthwise and dip in lemon water to prevent browning. Place artichoke halves around chicken and drizzle with remaining lemon water (water keeps vegetables from burning until chicken releases its juices). Spray vegetables lightly with olive oil nonstick spray.

6 Roast chicken and vegetables, stirring vegetables twice and adding ¼ cup of water each time, until instant-read thermometer inserted into thigh registers 165°F, about 1 hour 20 minutes. Remove vegetables from pan when tender, after about 1 hour. Transfer vegetables to large bowl. Add remaining 2 tablespoons lemon juice, remaining 2 teaspoons lemon zest, and remaining ¼ teaspoon salt and toss to coat. Cover to keep warm.

7 Place chicken on platter, cover loosely with foil, and let stand 10 minutes before carving. Carve chicken and divide chicken and vegetables evenly among 6 plates. Remove skin before eating.

5 **SmartPoints value per serving** (⅙ of chicken, 4 artichoke halves, and ¾ cup potatoes) 284 Cal, 5 g Total Fat, 1 g Sat Fat, 381 mg Sod, 27 g Total Carb, 2 g Sugar, 7 g Fib, 32 g Prot.

Red curry roast chicken with coconut sauce

Gluten Free   **Serves 8**

Spicy red curry paste seasons the chicken and the sauce in this Thai-inspired recipe. Definitely not your grandmother's roast chicken! Serve it with brown rice and steamed vegetables for a meal that updates the classic chicken dinner.

2	**lemongrass stalks, trimmed**
⅓	**cup chopped fresh cilantro, plus cilantro sprigs for garnish**
⅓	**cup chopped fresh mint**
1	**tablespoon grated peeled fresh ginger plus ¼ cup sliced ginger**
¾	**teaspoon salt**
1	**(4½-pound) whole chicken, giblets removed**
1	**lime, halved**
2½	**tablespoons Thai red curry paste**
1	**tablespoon plus 1 cup low-fat coconut milk**
1	**cup chicken broth**
1	**teaspoon packed brown sugar**
¼	**cup chopped dry-roasted salted peanuts**

Lime wedges

1 Preheat oven to 425°F. Set rack in medium roasting pan. Spray rack and pan with nonstick spray.

2 Grate 1 lemongrass stalk. Stir together grated lemongrass, the chopped cilantro, mint, grated ginger, and salt in cup. With your fingers, loosen skin on chicken breasts, legs, and thighs. Rub herb mixture on meat under skin; press skin back into place. Cut remaining lemongrass stalk into thirds. Place lime halves, lemongrass pieces, and sliced ginger inside chicken cavity.

3 Tuck wings under chicken and tie legs together with kitchen string. Stir together 1 tablespoon curry paste and 1 tablespoon coconut milk in another cup; rub all over chicken. Place chicken on rack, breast side up. Roast until instant-read thermometer inserted into thigh registers 165°F, about 1½ hours.

4 Transfer chicken to cutting board and let stand about 10 minutes.

5 Strain pan juices into measuring cup and skim off visible fat. Set roasting pan over 2 burners. Add remaining 1½ tablespoons curry paste and cook over low heat, stirring frequently, until fragrant, about 1 minute. Add pan juices and broth and bring to boil over high heat, stirring with wooden spoon to scrape up browned bits from bottom of pan. Reduce heat and cook, stirring occasionally, until broth is reduced to ¾ cup, about 5 minutes. Stir in remaining 1 cup coconut milk and the brown sugar; simmer until heated through.

6 Carve chicken into 8 pieces. Sprinkle with peanuts and cilantro sprigs and serve with sauce and lime wedges. Remove skin before eating.

5 **SmartPoints value per serving** (1 piece chicken and generous 2 tablespoons sauce): 218 Cal, 8 g Total Fat, 3 g Sat Fat, 435 mg Sod, 7 g Total Carb, 2 g Sugar, 1 g Fib, 29 g Prot.

Butterflied roast chicken with herbed potatoes

Gluten Free   Serves 6

Butterflying a chicken—removing the backbone, and opening up the chicken so it lies flat—ensures that it cooks evenly and stays juicy.

1	**(3½-pound) whole chicken, giblets removed**
1	**teaspoon salt**
¾	**teaspoon black pepper**
3	**baking potatoes, scrubbed, each cut into 8 wedges**
12	**small shallots, peeled**
8	**large garlic cloves, peeled**
2	**tablespoons chopped fresh rosemary or thyme**
1	**tablespoon olive oil**

1 Preheat oven to 400°F. Spray medium roasting pan with olive oil nonstick spray.

2 With kitchen scissors, cut down along each side of backbone of chicken and discard backbone or save for stock. Place chicken, opened flat, in roasting pan. Sprinkle chicken on both sides with ½ teaspoon salt and ½ teaspoon pepper. Arrange chicken in pan, skin side up; spray chicken with olive oil nonstick spray.

3 Roast chicken until instant-read thermometer inserted into thigh registers 165°F, about 1 hour.

4 Meanwhile, spray medium baking dish with olive oil nonstick spray. Combine potatoes, shallots, garlic, rosemary, remaining ½ teaspoon salt, and remaining ¼ teaspoon pepper in baking dish; drizzle with oil and toss to coat. Spread potatoes to form even layer. After chicken has roasted 15 minutes, put potatoes in oven and roast until potatoes are crisp and tender, about 45 minutes. Transfer to serving bowl.

5 Transfer chicken to cutting board and let stand 10 minutes. Carve chicken and arrange on platter. Skim off any fat from pan juices; pour pan juices over chicken. Serve potato mixture alongside. Remove skin before eating.

(5) **SmartPoints value per serving** (⅙ of chicken, about 2 tablespoons pan juices, and ⅙ of vegetables): 300 Cal, 7 g Total Fat, 1 g Sat Fat, 399 mg Sod, 28 g Total Carb, 4 g Sugar, 3 g Fib, 31 g Prot.

Roast capon with bourbon sauce

Gluten Free   Serves 12

Mustard, brown sugar, and thyme are combined to make a flavorful rub for this stunning roast capon.

⅓   cup packed brown sugar

1   tablespoon plus
     2 teaspoons coarse-grained
     Dijon mustard

1   tablespoon chopped
     fresh thyme

1   teaspoon salt

½   teaspoon black pepper

1   (8-pound) capon, giblets
     removed

2   large shallots, minced

¼   cup bourbon

¾   cup chicken broth

1 Preheat oven to 350°F. Set rack in medium roasting pan. Spray rack and pan with nonstick spray.

2 Combine brown sugar, 1 tablespoon mustard, the thyme, salt, and pepper in small bowl. With your fingers, loosen skin on capon breasts, legs, and thighs. Rub sugar mixture on meat under skin; press skin back into place.

3 Tuck wings under capon and tie legs together with kitchen string. Place capon on rack, breast side up. Roast until instant-read thermometer inserted into thigh registers 165°F, 2½–3 hours.

4 Carefully tilt capon upright to allow juices inside cavity to pour into pan. Transfer capon to cutting board and let stand about 15 minutes.

5 Meanwhile, remove rack from roasting pan. Strain pan juices into measuring cup and skim off visible fat.

6 Set roasting pan over 2 burners over medium heat. Add shallots and cook over medium heat, stirring frequently, until shallots are softened, about 2 minutes. Stir in bourbon and remaining 2 teaspoons mustard and bring to boil. Add pan juices and broth; bring to boil over high heat, stirring with wooden spoon to scrape up browned bits from bottom of pan. Carve capon into 12 pieces and serve with pan sauce. Remove skin before eating.

 SmartPoints value per serving (¹⁄₁₂ of capon and about 2 tablespoons sauce): 227 Cal, 5 g Total Fat, 1 g Sat Fat, 291 mg Sod, 8 g Total Carb, 7 g Sugar, 0 g Fib, 32 g Prot.

Cook's tip

Capon, a large male chicken, is prized for its exceptional flavor and generous amount of extra-moist white meat. Most capons are sold frozen, so it pays to plan ahead (allow at least 2 days to thaw the bird in the refrigerator). If capon is not available at your butcher or specialty store, order online at www.roastcapon.com.

**Roast capon with
bourbon sauce**

Roast capon with pomegranate glaze

Serves 12

5 **tablespoons pomegranate molasses**
1 **tablespoon Dijon mustard**
1 **tablespoon fennel seeds, crushed**
1 **tablespoon ground cumin**
2 **teaspoons ground coriander**
2 **teaspoons paprika**
1 **teaspoon salt**
½ **teaspoon black pepper**
½ **teaspoon cinnamon**
1 **(8-pound) capon, giblets removed**
2 **large shallots, minced**
2 **tablespoons all-purpose flour**
1 **cup chicken broth**

1 Preheat oven to 350°F. Set rack in medium roasting pan. Spray rack and pan with nonstick spray.

2 To make glaze, stir together pomegranate molasses and mustard in small bowl. Set aside 2 tablespoons of glaze for brushing during final 15 minutes of roasting.

3 Stir together fennel seeds, cumin, coriander, paprika, salt, pepper, and cinnamon in cup. With your fingers, loosen skin on capon breasts, legs, and thighs. Rub spice mixture on meat under skin; press skin back into place.

4 Tuck wings under capon and tie legs together with kitchen string. Place capon on rack, breast side up, and brush with 4 tablespoons glaze. Pour 3 cups water into roasting pan. Roast until instant-read thermometer inserted into thigh registers 165°F, 2½–3 hours, adding more water to pan if necessary if liquid evaporates, and brushing capon with reserved glaze during last 15 minutes of roasting.

5 Carefully tilt capon upright to allow juices inside cavity to pour into pan. Transfer capon to cutting board and let stand about 15 minutes.

6 Meanwhile, remove rack from roasting pan. Strain pan juices into measuring cup and discard solids. Skim off visible fat. Set pan over 2 burners over medium heat. Add shallots and cook, stirring frequently, until shallots are softened, about 2 minutes. Add flour and cook, stirring constantly, 1 minute. Add broth and pan juices; bring to boil over high heat, stirring with wooden spoon to scrape up browned bits from bottom of pan. Carve capon into 12 pieces and serve with pan sauce. Remove skin before eating.

 SmartPoints value per serving (¹⁄₁₂ of capon and about 2 tablespoons pan sauce): 223 Cal, 5 g Total Fat, 1 g Sat Fat, 318 mg Sod, 9 g Total Carb, 5 g Sugar, 1 g Fib, 33 g Prot.

Roast capon with orange and root veggies

Serves 12

2	navel oranges
2	tablespoons butter, softened
2	shallots, minced
2	teaspoons salt
1	teaspoon black pepper
1	(8-pound) capon, giblets removed
6	fresh or dried bay leaves
3	pounds carrots, cut into 2 x 1-inch chunks
2	pounds parsnips, cut into 2 x 1-inch chunks
2	large red onions, cut through root end into 12 wedges
¼	cup chopped fresh flat-leaf parsley
2	shallots, minced
2	tablespoons all-purpose flour
¾	cup chicken broth

1 Adjust oven racks to upper and lower thirds of oven. Preheat oven to 375°F. Set rack in medium roasting pan. Spray rack and pan with nonstick spray.

2 From oranges, grate 2 teaspoons zest. Cut oranges in half and squeeze enough juice from 1 to equal ½ cup (reserve juice for sauce). Cut remaining orange into quarters. Stir together butter, shallots, orange zest, 1 teaspoon salt, and ½ teaspoon pepper in small bowl. With your fingers, loosen skin on capon breasts, legs, and thighs. Rub shallot mixture on meat under skin. Place 1 bay leaf under skin of each breast half and 1 bay leaf under skin of each thigh and press skin back into place. Place orange wedges and remaining 2 bay leaves inside chicken cavity.

3 Tuck wings under capon and tie legs together with kitchen string. Place capon on roasting rack, breast side up. Place capon on lower oven rack and roast 1½ hours.

4 Transfer 2 tablespoons pan drippings from capon to large rimmed baking sheet. Add carrots, parsnips, onion, and remaining 1 teaspoon salt and remaining ½ teaspoon pepper; toss to coat. Place vegetables on upper oven rack and roast until instant-read thermometer inserted into thigh registers 165°F and vegetables are tender, about 1 hour, stirring vegetables once.

5 Carefully tilt capon upright to allow juices inside cavity to pour into pan. Transfer capon to cutting board and let stand about 15 minutes. Transfer vegetables to bowl, sprinkle with parsley and keep warm.

6 Meanwhile, remove rack from roasting pan. Strain pan juices into measuring cup and discard solids. Skim off visible fat. Set pan over 2 burners over medium heat. Add shallots and cook, stirring frequently, until shallots are softened, about 2 minutes. Add flour and cook, stirring constantly, 1 minute. Add broth, reserved orange juice, and pan juices and bring to boil over high heat, stirring with wooden spoon to scrape up browned bits from bottom of pan. Carve capon into 12 pieces and serve with pan sauce. Remove skin before eating.

(6) **SmartPoints value per serving** (¹⁄₁₂ of capon, about ⅔ cup vegetables, and 2 tablespoons sauce): 336 Cal, 7 g Total Fat, 2 g Sat Fat, 522 mg Sod, 32 g Total Carb, 13 g Sugar, 8 g Fib, 35 g Prot.

**Herbed cornish
hens under a brick**

Herbed cornish hens under a brick

Gluten Free   **Serves 4**

The purpose of the bricks is to weigh the hens down to help them cook evenly and get direct contact with the pan so they brown and caramelize as they cook. It's unusual, but it's the trick to the juiciest most flavorful cornish hens you've ever had.

Grated zest and juice of 1 lemon

1   **tablespoon chopped fresh flat-leaf parsley**

1½ **teaspoons chopped fresh thyme**

1½ **teaspoons chopped fresh rosemary**

1   **small shallot, minced**

½   **teaspoon salt**

⅛   **teaspoon cayenne**

2   **(1¼-pound) cornish hens, giblets removed**

2   **lemons, halved**

1 Stir together lemon zest and juice, parsley, thyme, rosemary, shallot, salt, and cayenne in small bowl.

2 With kitchen scissors, cut down along each side of backbone of each hen and discard backbone or save for stock.

3 With your fingers, loosen skin on breasts, legs, and thighs. Spread lemon mixture on meat under skin; press skin back into place. Place hens in large zip-close plastic bag. Squeeze out air and seal bag; refrigerate at least 4 hours or up to 8 hours.

4 Meanwhile, spray large grill pan with nonstick spray and set over medium heat. Wrap 2 clean bricks in double layer of foil.

5 Remove hens from bag and discard liquid. Place hens, opened flat and skin side down, in grill pan and place bricks on top. Grill until hens are golden, about 12 minutes. Turn hens. Place bricks back on top of hens. Grill until instant-read thermometer inserted into thigh registers 165°F, 12–15 minutes longer.

6 Lightly spray lemon halves with olive oil nonstick spray. Place cut side down in grill pan and grill until well-marked, about 4 minutes. Transfer hens to platter; let stand 5 minutes. Remove skin before eating. Serve with lemon halves.

Note: If you don't have bricks on hand, put your heaviest cast iron skillet on top of the hens instead.

4 **SmartPoints value per serving** (½ hen): 226 Cal, 6 g Total Fat, 2 g Sat Fat, 420 mg Sod, 2 g Total Carb, 1 g Sugar, 0 g Fib, 38 g Prot

Maple-glazed cornish hens with spinach and pear

Gluten Free   Serves 4

Wild rice is a classic accompaniment to cornish hens and would pair perfectly with this dish. You can enjoy ½ cup of cooked wild rice for 2 SmartPoints.

4	teaspoons pure maple syrup
2	teaspoons unsalted butter, melted
1	(10-ounce) box frozen chopped spinach, thawed and squeezed dry
1	large Bosc pear, peeled, cored, and diced
2	tablespoons chopped pecans
1	shallot, finely chopped
¾	teaspoon salt
¼	teaspoon ground nutmeg
¼	teaspoon black pepper
2	(1¼-pound) cornish hens, giblets removed

1 Preheat oven to 350°F. Spray large rimmed baking pan with nonstick spray.

2 Stir together 3 teaspoons maple syrup and 1 teaspoon butter in small cup until blended well; set aside.

3 Combine remaining 1 teaspoon maple syrup, remaining 1 teaspoon butter, the spinach, pear, pecans, shallot, salt, nutmeg, and pepper in medium bowl. Divide spinach mixture into 2 mounds in center of prepared pan, spacing 2 inches apart.

4 With kitchen scissors, cut down along both sides of backbone of each hen and discard backbones. Flatten hens and place each hen, skin side up, on top of spinach mixture. Brush hens with maple-syrup mixture. Roast until instant-read thermometer inserted into thigh registers 165°F, about 45 minutes.

5 Serve hens with spinach mixture. Remove skin before eating.

6 **SmartPoints value per serving** (½ stuffed hen and ½ cup spinach mixture): 332 Cal, 11 g Total Fat, 3 g Sat Fat, 618 mg Sod, 17 g Total Carb, 10 g Sugar, 4 g Fib, 41 g Prot.

Let's do this together

WW member Nancy Kunak is an expert with healthy food shopping strategies. "I fill up my cart with fresh fruits and vegetables by hitting the produce aisle first," she says. "Then I pick up other healthy foods like chicken breast and fresh seafood, avoiding the cookie aisle altogether."

Fennel-spiced roast turkey with mushroom gravy

Serves 12

1 (10- to 12-pound) whole turkey
1 tablespoon fennel seeds
1 tablespoon chopped fresh thyme
3 garlic cloves, minced
3 teaspoons olive oil
¾ teaspoon salt
2¼ cups chicken broth
¼ cup dry sherry
½ pound shiitake mushrooms, stems discarded, caps sliced
2 tablespoons all-purpose flour

1 Place oven rack in lower third of oven. Preheat oven to 450°F. Place rack in large roasting pan and spray with nonstick spray. Remove neck and giblets from cavity of turkey and discard (or save for another use).

2 Pulse fennel seeds, thyme, garlic, 1 teaspoon oil, and salt in mini–food processor or spice grinder until paste forms. With your fingers, loosen skin on turkey breast. Rub fennel mixture evenly on meat under skin; press skin back into place. Tuck wings under turkey and tie legs together with kitchen string. Place turkey, breast side up, on prepared rack in roasting pan. Pour 1 cup broth into bottom of pan; roast turkey 20 minutes. Reduce oven temperature to 350°F. Continue roasting until instant-read thermometer inserted into thigh registers 165°F, about 2½ hours longer (cover turkey loosely with foil if it begins to get too brown). Transfer turkey to cutting board. Cover loosely with foil and let stand 20 minutes.

3 Meanwhile, to make gravy, pour drippings and juices from roasting pan into large measuring cup. Let stand 5 minutes; skim off fat and discard. Set aside.

4 Set roasting pan over 2 burners over medium-high heat. Add sherry to pan and bring to boil, stirring with wooden spoon to scrape up browned bits from bottom of pan. Add remaining 1¼ cups broth to pan and return to boil. Strain mixture through fine wire-mesh strainer into measuring cup with drippings. Discard solids.

5 Heat remaining 2 teaspoons oil in large skillet over medium heat. Add mushrooms and cook, stirring occasionally, until mushrooms are tender, about 4 minutes. Stir in flour; cook, stirring constantly, 1 minute. Add sherry mixture and cook, stirring frequently, until gravy bubbles and thickens, about 2 minutes.

6 Remove skin and carve into 24 slices. Serve turkey with gravy.

5 **SmartPoints value per serving** (2 slices turkey and 3 tablespoons gravy): 346 Cal, 7 g Total Fat, 1 g Sat Fat, 612 mg Sod, 4 g Total Carb, 0 g Sugar, 1 g Fib, 64 g Prot.

Honey herb roast turkey breast with pan gravy

Serves 10

If you have leftover sage and thyme from this recipe, add them to roasted vegetables like white or sweet potatoes, butternut squash, turnips, or rutabagas. They're also both delicious in vegetable soups and white bean dishes.

2   **tablespoons honey**

2   **tablespoons chopped fresh sage**

1   **tablespoon chopped fresh thyme**

1   **tablespoon softened butter**

1   **teaspoon Dijon mustard**

½   **teaspoon salt**

¼   **plus ⅛ teaspoon black pepper**

1   **(4½-pound) turkey breast with ribs**

4   **cups chicken broth**

2   **tablespoons all-purpose flour**

1 Preheat oven to 375°F. Spray medium roasting pan with nonstick spray.

2 Stir honey, sage, thyme, butter, mustard, salt, and ¼ teaspoon pepper together in small bowl. With your fingers, loosen skin on turkey breast. Spread most of the honey mixture on meat under skin; press skin back into place. Rub remaining mixture all over skin.

3 Place turkey breast in pan. Pour 1½ cups broth into pan. Roast until instant-read thermometer inserted into center of breast registers 165°F, about 2 hours. Transfer turkey breast to cutting board, cover loosely with foil, and let stand 10 minutes.

4 Meanwhile, to make gravy, drain all but 1 tablespoon drippings from pan. Set pan over 2 burners over medium-high heat; sprinkle in flour and cook, whisking constantly until well blended, about 2 minutes. Whisk in remaining 2½ cups broth and cook, whisking constantly until mixture comes to boil. Reduce heat and simmer, whisking occasionally, until gravy is reduced to 2 cups, about 3 minutes. Stir in remaining ⅛ teaspoon pepper.

5 Discard ribs and skin from turkey breast. Cut turkey into 20 slices and serve with gravy.

 **SmartPoints value per serving** (2 slices turkey and about 3 tablespoons gravy): 207 Cal, 4 g Total Fat, 2 g Sat Fat, 750 mg Sod, 6 g Total Carb, 4 g Sugar, 0 g Fib, 36 g Prot.

Turkey breast with apples, fennel, and barley

Serves 4

1   **tablespoon Dijon mustard**

1   **teaspoon packed brown sugar**

½   **teaspoon soy sauce**

1   **(1½-pound) boneless turkey breast**

3   **Golden Delicious apples, peeled, cored, and cut into ¾-inch-thick wedges**

1   **large fennel bulb, cut into ¾-inch wedges**

1   **red onion, sliced**

¾   **cup quick-cooking barley**

¾   **cup water**

⅛   **teaspoon salt**

1   **small head radicchio, thinly sliced**

1   Preheat oven to 425°F. Line bottom of broiler pan with foil; spray foil with nonstick spray.

2   Mix mustard, sugar, and soy sauce together in small bowl. Place turkey on broiler pan; spread mustard mixture evenly over turkey. Scatter apples, fennel, and onion in pan. Roast until instant-read thermometer inserted into center of turkey registers 165°F and vegetables and apples are tender, 40–45 minutes.

3   Meanwhile, mix barley, water, and salt in large microwavable bowl. Cover with vented plastic wrap and microwave on High 8 minutes. Add radicchio, cover, and microwave until barley is tender, about 2 minutes.

4   Transfer turkey to cutting board and let rest 5 minutes. Cut into 12 slices. Serve with apples, vegetables, and barley. Remove skin before eating.

4   **SmartPoints value per serving** (3 slices turkey, 1 cup vegetables and apples, and ½ cup barley): 459 Cal, 4 g Total Fat, 1 g Sat Fat, 409 mg Sod, 60 g Total Carb, 16 g Sugar, 12 g Fib, 47 g Prot.

Let's do this together

"Get rid of the clutter," advises WW member Kate Leissler, who finds that having fewer tools and less equipment saves her time in the kitchen. "If you've got items you only think you might need, put them in a box in the basement. If you don't miss them after a month, get rid of them!"

Leek and herb–stuffed
bacon-wrapped turkey

Leek and herb–stuffed bacon-wrapped turkey

Gluten Free   Serves 12

Filled with a stuffing of leek, garlic, parsley, and rosemary, then wrapped in Italian bacon and roasted, this turkey breast tastes as good as it looks. The sliced roast topped with rosy pancetta slices makes this dish impressive—and easy—enough for any celebration.

1½	tablespoons olive oil
1	large leek, sliced (white and light green parts only)
1	large shallot, sliced
3	garlic cloves, sliced
1	tablespoon fresh rosemary leaves
2	cups packed fresh flat-leaf parsley leaves
1¼	teaspoons kosher salt
2	(2-pound) boneless turkey breast halves, skin removed
½	teaspoon black pepper
1	(3-ounce) package sliced pancetta

1 Preheat oven to 375°F. Spray large rimmed baking sheet with non-stick spray.

2 To make stuffing, heat 1 tablespoon oil in medium skillet over medium heat. Add leek, shallot, garlic, and rosemary and cook, stirring occasionally, until leek softens, about 5 minutes. Remove pan from heat and cool. Combine leek mixture, parsley, remaining ½ tablespoon oil, and ¼ teaspoon salt in food processor and pulse until finely chopped.

3 Working with one at a time, place turkey breast half on cutting board, smooth side down. Holding knife parallel to board, slice meat horizontally, stopping about ¾ inch from edge (don't cut all the way through). Open up turkey like a book and cover with 2 large sheets of plastic wrap. With heavy rolling pin, pound turkey until about ¾-inch thick. Discard plastic wrap.

4 Sprinkle both sides of turkey breasts with remaining 1 teaspoon salt and the pepper and spread evenly with filling, leaving a ½-inch border. Starting with one long side, roll up each turkey breast jelly-roll style. Place turkey breasts seam side down and cover top with pancetta, overlapping slices slightly. With kitchen string, tie turkey breasts tightly at 1½-inch intervals.

5 Place turkey in prepared pan and roast until instant-read thermometer inserted into breast registers 165°F, 1 hour–1 hour 10 minutes. Let stand 10 minutes. Cut and discard string; carve each turkey breast half into slices.

(2) **SmartPoints value per serving** (about 2 slices): 230 Cal, 7 g Total Fat, 2 g Sat Fat, 427 mg Sod, 3 g Total Carb, 1 g Sugar, 1 g Fib, 37 g Prot.

Turkey tortilla
wedges with
arugula and
pine nuts,
page 37

Recipes by SmartPoints value

0 SmartPoints

Basic spice rub, 45
Chicken with grapefruit-mint salsa, 59
Coffee rub, 45
Indian-spiced chicken with mango raita, 7
Montreal chicken rub, 45

1 SmartPoints

Asian chicken-mushroom soup, 20
Chicken and eggplant stir-fry with snow peas, 125
Chicken packets with zucchini and tomatoes, 51
Chicken with fresh tomato sauce, 122
Chicken with tomato, olive, and feta salad, 60
Chicken with tomato-zucchini salad, 48
Crispy chicken with red pepper sauce, 2
Ginger meatball and vegetable soup, 168
Indian-spiced yogurt marinade, 45
Moroccan turkey and chickpea soup, 32
Mustard-glazed chicken salad with mango
    and lime, 80
Peruvian chicken marinade, 45
Southwest turkey and vegetable soup, 144
Turkey-lentil curry, 34
Turkey, red bean, and chipotle pepper chili, 135
Turkey-tomatillo chili, 143

2 SmartPoints

Asian chicken with carrot-cucumber slaw, 55
Basic lemon-herb marinade, 45
Cajun chicken with minted cucumber-tomato relish, 4
Chicken and asparagus stir-fry with basil, 25
Chicken and corn salad with yogurt-lime dressing, 47
Chicken and veggie kebabs with romesco sauce, 62
Chicken stir-fry with black bean sauce, 23
Chicken with creamy tarragon-mushroom sauce, 11
Chicken with cucumber, orange, and olive salad, 53
Chicken with orange-avocado salsa, 13
Greek turkey meatballs, 177
Grilled chicken with shishito peppers, 56
Grilled chicken with tomato-anchovy sauce, 54
Grilled turkey with watermelon and herb salad, 73

Honey herb roast turkey breast with pan gravy, 200
Leek and herb–stuffed bacon-wrapped turkey, 203
Roasted Greek-style chicken and vegetables, 120
Thai turkey and broccoli stir-fry, 140
Tomato–stuffed chicken with roasted fennel, 114
Turkey mushroom-barley soup with dill, 165

3 SmartPoints

Asian peanut chicken salad, 90
Brown sugar–brined chicken, 42
Chicken niçoise salad with tarragon-olive
    vinaigrette, 78
Chicken vegetable noodle bowl, 126
Chicken vegetable udon soup, 121
Chicken with tomatoes, apricots, and chickpeas, 12
Grilled chicken salad with ginger-honey dressing, 18
Lentil and chorizo soup with kale, 139
Parmesan chicken with fennel-arugula salad, 17
Roast chicken with meyer lemons and
    shallot sauce, 186
Rosemary-garlic baked chicken, 116
Stovetop cassoulet, 161
Succotash chicken salad with avocado dressing, 89
Tuscan sausage and bean stew, 145
Very veggie turkey meat loaf, 171
Vietnamese chicken thighs with mango relish, 61

4 SmartPoints

Buttermilk-marinated oven-fried chicken, 152
Chicken and grape salad, 86
Chicken, spinach, and quinoa salad with olives, 84
Chicken with orange and basil gremolata, 64
Creamy chicken and corn chowder, 19
Herbed cornish hens under a brick, 197
Korean chicken and rice bowls, 28
Mojito barbecued chicken, 46
Oven-barbecued chicken with mop sauce, 148
Roast capon with pomegranate glaze, 194
Sautéed chicken thighs with lemon and capers, 26
Soft turkey tacos with smoky tomatillo salsa, 68
Stir-fry chicken with cashews, 22

Sweet-and-smoky roast chicken, 182
Tandoori chicken skewers with roasted
   vegetables, 136
Turkey breast with apples, fennel and barley, 201

5 SmartPoints

Almond chicken cutlets with tangy cilantro slaw, 14
Butterflied roast chicken with herbed potatoes, 191
Chicken milanese with arugula salad, 153
Chicken pot pie with chive biscuits, 167
Chicken ratatouille with penne, 155
Chicken salad with farro and squash, 83
Chicken sausages with bean-and-tomato salad, 31
Creole jambalaya, 156
Curried turkey and lentil burgers, 108
Fennel-spiced roast turkey with mushroom gravy, 199
Grilled chicken with cucumber and herb salad, 67
Grilled turkey tacos with strawberry salsa, 70
Lemon chicken with white beans and
   stuffed peppers, 133
Lemon-rosemary chicken with radicchio, 128
Moroccan-style chicken with olives, 65
Open-face cobb salad sandwiches, 102
Open-face Greek turkey burgers, 111
Red curry roast chicken with coconut sauce, 190
Roast capon with bourbon sauce, 192
Roast chermoula chicken with butternut squash, 134
Roast chicken and vegetables provençal, 185
Roast chicken with artichokes and potatoes, 189
Roast chicken with prosciutto stuffing, 180
Rosemary-prosciutto chicken with potatoes, 119
Saffron and tomato chicken with olive couscous, 8
Slow cooker balsamic-braised chicken with kale, 129
Thai chicken salad, 92
Thai ginger chicken burgers, 103
Turkey cutlets with couscous-cucumber salad, 71

6 SmartPoints

Braised chicken with potatoes and artichokes, 131
Chicken and sausage paella, 157
Chicken bahn mi sandwiches, 101
Chicken panzanella with peppers and pine nuts, 85
Chicken sandwiches with pickled vegetable slaw, 104
Hearty chicken with parsley dumplings, 150
Maple-glazed cornish hens with spinach
   and pear, 198
Orecchiette with sausage and broccoli rabe, 39

Rigatoni with turkey bolognese, 175
Roast capon with orange and root veggies, 195
Smoky turkey, quinoa, and roasted red pepper
   salad, 95
Turkey club salad with creamy peppercorn
   dressing, 96
Turkey couscous salad with dried fruit and
   pine nuts, 98
Turkey fattoush salad, 93
Turkey sausage and roasted potato salad, 99

7 SmartPoints

Chicken, caramelized onion, and goat
   cheese pizza, 158
Penne with sausage, white beans, and kale, 33
Slow cooker chicken stew with roasted-
   pepper rouille, 130
Spicy farfalle with chicken chorizo and chickpeas, 27
Wild mushroom and sausage risotto, 162

8 SmartPoints

Chicken with couscous-mango salad, 50
Grilled sausage and onion salad with figs, 75
Turkey, spinach, and goat cheese enchiladas, 172
Turkey, spinach, and mushroom lasagna, 174

9 SmartPoints

Chicken, corn, and black bean pizza, 164
Turkey tortilla wedges with arugula and
   pine nuts, 37

10 SmartPoints

Chutney chicken sliders, 107

12 SmartPoints

Chicken sausage and mushroom hoagies, 109

Index

A

Almonds
Almond chicken cutlets with tangy cilantro slaw, 14
Saffron and tomato chicken with olive couscous, 8

Anchovy: Grilled chicken with tomato-, sauce, 54

Apples
Stovetop cassoulet, 161
Turkey breast with apples, fennel, and barley, 201

Apricots, Chicken with tomatoes, and chickpeas, 12

Artichokes
Braised chicken with potatoes and artichokes, 131
Roast chicken with artichokes and potatoes, 189

Arugula
Chicken Milanese with arugula salad, 153
Chicken panzanella with peppers and pine nuts, 85
Chicken with couscous-mango salad, 50
Parmesan chicken with fennel-arugula salad, 17
Turkey couscous salad with dried fruit and pine nuts, 98
Turkey tortilla wedges with arugula and pine nuts, 37
Tuscan sausage and bean stew, 145

Asian chicken-mushroom soup, 20
Asian chicken with carrot-cucumber slaw, 55
Asian peanut chicken salad, 90

Asparagus, Chicken and, stir-fry with basil, 25

Avocado
Chicken with orange-avocado salsa, 13

Grilled turkey tacos with strawberry salsa, 70
Open-face cobb salad sandwiches, 102
Succotash chicken salad with avocado dressing, 89

B

Bacon. *See also* Turkey bacon
Tomato-stuffed chicken with roasted fennel, 108

Basic lemon-herb marinade, 45
Basic spice rub, 45

Basil
Chicken and asparagus stir-fry with basil, 25
Chicken packets with zucchini and tomatoes, 51
Chicken with fresh tomato sauce, 122
Chicken with orange and basil gremolata, 64
Crispy chicken with red pepper sauce, 2
Grilled chicken with shishito peppers, 56
Lemon chicken with white beans and stuffed peppers, 133
Penne with sausage, white beans, and kale, 33

Beans. *See* Black beans; Cannellini beans; Green beans; Lima beans; Red kidney beans; White beans

Bean sprouts: Grilled chicken salad with ginger-honey dressing, 18

Bell peppers
Chicken and asparagus stir-fry with basil, 25
Chicken and sausage paella, 157

Chicken and veggie kebabs with romesco sauce, 62
Chicken panzanella with peppers and pine nuts, 85
Chicken ratatouille with penne, 155
Chicken sandwiches with pickled vegetable slaw, 104
Chicken stir-fry with black bean sauce, 23
Chicken vegetable noodle bowl, 126
Chicken with cucumber, orange, and olive salad, 53
Creamy chicken and corn chowder, 19
Ginger meatball and vegetable soup, 168
Lemon chicken with white beans and stuffed peppers, 133
Stir-fry chicken with cashews, 22
Thai chicken salad, 92
Turkey, red bean, and chipotle pepper chili, 135
Turkey-tomatillo chili, 143

Bibb lettuce
Chutney chicken sliders, 107
Curried turkey and lentil burgers, 108
Mustard-glazed chicken salad with mango and lime, 80
Open-face Greek turkey burgers, 111

Biscuits, Chicken pot pie with chive, 167

Black beans, Chicken, corn, and, pizza, 165

Black bean sauce: Chicken stir-fry with Asian, 23

Blue cheese: Open-face cobb salad sandwiches, 102

Boston lettuce

Succotash chicken salad with avocado dressing, 89

Thai chicken salad, 92

Braised chicken with potatoes and artichokes, 131

Broccoli

Orecchiette with sausage and broccoli rabe, 39

Thai turkey and broccoli stir-fry, 140

Brown rice: Korean chicken and rice bowls, 28

Brown sugar–brined chicken, 42

Burgers

Chutney chicken sliders, 107

Curried turkey and lentil burgers, 108

Open-face Greek turkey burgers, 111

Thai ginger-chicken burgers, 103

Butterflied roast chicken with herbed potatoes, 191

Buttermilk-marinated oven-fried chicken, 152

Butternut squash

Chicken salad with farro and squash, 83

Roast chermoula chicken with butternut squash, 134

C

Cabbage. *See* Napa cabbage; Red cabbage

Cajun chicken with minty cucumber-tomato relish, 4

Cannellini beans

Chicken sausages with bean-and-tomato salad, 31

Lemon chicken with white beans and stuffed peppers, 133

Penne with sausage, white beans, and kale, 33

Stovetop cassoulet, 161

Turkey-tomatillo chili, 143

Tuscan sausage and bean stew, 145

Capers

Grilled chicken with tomato-anchovy sauce, 54

Sautéed chicken thighs with lemon and capers, 26

Capon, x

Roast capon with bourbon sauce, 192

Roast capon with orange and root veggies, 195

Roast capon with pomegranate glaze, 194

Carrots

Asian chicken with carrot-cucumber slaw, 55

Asian peanut chicken salad, 90

Chicken sandwiches with pickled vegetable slaw, 104

Ginger meatball and vegetable soup, 168

Hearty chicken with parsley dumplings, 150

Korean chicken and rice bowls, 28

Roast capon with orange and root veggies, 195

Stovetop cassoulet, 161

Thai chicken salad, 92

Cashews, Stir-fry chicken with, 22

Cassoulet, Stovetop, 161

Cauliflower: Tandoori chicken skewers with roasted vegetables, 136

Cheese. *See* Feta cheese; Goat cheese; Mozzarella cheese; Parmesan cheese; Ricotta; Romano cheese

Cherry tomatoes. *See also* Grape tomatoes

Cajun chicken with minty cucumber-tomato relish, 4

Chicken, spinach, and quinoa salad with olives, 84

Chicken sausages with bean-and-tomato salad, 31

Chicken with tomato-zucchini salad, 48

Grilled chicken with cucumber and herb salad, 67

Roasted Greek-style chicken and vegetables, 120

Rosemary-prosciutto chicken with potatoes, 119

Succotash chicken salad with avocado dressing, 89

Turkey tortilla wedges with arugula and pine nuts, 37

Chicken, ground

Chutney chicken sliders, 107

Korean chicken and rice bowls, 28

Thai chicken salad, 92

Thai ginger-chicken burgers, 103

Chicken sausage

Chicken sausage and mushroom hoagies, 109

Chicken sausages with bean-and-tomato salad, 31

Grilled sausage and onion salad with figs, 75

Lentil and chorizo soup with kale, 139

Spicy farfalle with chicken chorizo and chickpeas, 27

Tuscan sausage and bean stew, 145

Wild mushroom and sausage risotto, 162

Chickpeas

Chicken with tomatoes, apricots, and chickpeas, 12

Moroccan turkey and chickpea soup, 32

Spicy farfalle with chicken chorizo and chickpeas, 27

Chutney chicken sliders, 107

Coffee rub, 45

Corn

Chicken, corn, and black bean pizza, 165

Chicken and corn salad with yogurt-lime dressing, 47

Creamy chicken and corn chowder, 19

Southwest turkey and vegetable soup, 144

Succotash chicken salad with avocado dressing, 89

Cornish hens, x

Herbed Cornish hens under a brick, 197

Maple-glazed Cornish hens with spinach and pear, 198

Couscous

Chicken with couscous-mango salad, 50

Saffron and tomato chicken with olive couscous, 8

Turkey cutlets with couscous-cucumber salad, 71

Creamy chicken and corn chowder, 19

Creole Jambalaya, 156

Crispy chicken with red pepper sauce, 2

Cucumbers. See also English cucumbers

Grilled chicken with cucumber and herb salad, 67

Indian-spiced chicken with mango raita, 7

Succotash chicken salad with avocado dressing, 89

Turkey cutlets with couscous-cucumber salad, 71

Turkey fattoush salad, 93

Curried turkey and lentil burgers, 108

Curry, Turkey-lentil, 34

D

Dates: Turkey couscous salad with dried fruit and pine nuts, 98

Dumplings, Hearty chicken with parsley, 150

E

Easy dry rubs, 45

Edamame

Asian peanut chicken salad, 90

Chicken vegetable noodle bowl, 126

Eggplant

Chicken and eggplant stir-fry with snow peas, 125

Chicken ratatouille with penne, 155

Eggs: Chicken niçoise salad with tarragon-olive vinaigrette, 78

Enchiladas, Turkey, spinach, and goat cheese, 172

English cucumbers. See also Cucumbers

Asian chicken with carrot-cucumber slaw, 55

Asian peanut chicken salad, 90

Cajun chicken with minty cucumber-tomato relish, 4

Curried turkey and lentil burgers, 108

Korean chicken and rice bowls, 28

Open-face Greek turkey burgers, 111

Thai ginger-chicken burgers, 103

F

Farfalle, spicy, with chicken chorizo and chickpeas, 27

Farro, Chicken salad with, and squash, 83

Fattoush, Turkey, salad, 93

Fennel

Chicken Milanese with arugula salad, 153

Fennel-spiced roast turkey with mushroom gravy, 199

Tomato-stuffed chicken with roasted fennel, 108

Turkey breast with apples, fennel, and barley, 201

Feta cheese

Chicken with tomato, olive, and feta salad, 60

Grilled turkey with watermelon and herb salad, 73

Turkey tortilla wedges with arugula and pine nuts, 37

Figs, Grilled sausage and onion salad with, 75

G

Ginger meatball and vegetable soup, 168

Goat cheese

Chicken, caramelized onion, and goat cheese pizza, 158

Turkey, spinach, and goat cheese enchiladas, 172

Grapefruit, Chicken with,-mint salsa, 59

Grapes

Chicken salad with farro and squash, 83

Turkey couscous salad with dried fruit and pine nuts, 98

Grape tomatoes. See also Cherry tomatoes

Chicken Milanese with arugula salad, 153

Chicken with tomato, olive, and feta salad, 60

Chicken with tomato-zucchini salad, 48

Orecchiette with sausage and broccoli rabe, 39

Spicy farfalle with chicken chorizo and chickpeas, 27

Greek yogurt. *See also* Yogurt

Chicken and grape salad, 86

Chicken with creamy tarragon-mushroom sauce, 11

Indian-spiced chicken with mango raita, 7

Open-face Greek turkey burgers, 111

Turkey, red bean, and chipotle pepper chili, 135

Green beans

Chicken niçoise salad with tarragon-olive vinaigrette, 78

Chicken sausages with bean-and-tomato salad, 31

Grilled chicken salad with ginger-honey dressing, 18

Grilled chicken with cucumber and herb salad, 67

Grilled chicken with shishito peppers, 56

Grilled chicken with tomato-anchovy sauce, 54

Grilled sausage and onion salad with figs, 75

Grilled turkey tacos with strawberry salsa, 70

Grilled turkey with watermelon and herb salad, 73

H

Hearty chicken with parsley dumplings, 150

Herbed Cornish hens under a brick, 197

Honey herb roast turkey breast with pan gravy, 200

I

Indian-spiced chicken with mango raita, 7

Indian-spiced yogurt marinade, 45

J

Jalapeño peppers

Chicken with orange-avocado salsa, 13

Chicken with tomato-zucchini salad, 48

Roast chermoula chicken with butternut squash, 134

Thai turkey and broccoli stir-fry, 140

Vietnamese chicken thighs with mango relish, 61

Jambalaya, Creole, 156

K

Kale

Lentil and chorizo soup with kale, 139

Penne with sausage, white beans, and kale, 33

Skinless cooker balsamic-braised chicken with, 129

Spicy farfalle with chicken chorizo and chickpeas, 27

Turkey sausage and roasted potato salad, 99

Kebabs, Chicken and veggie, with romesco sauce, 62

Korean chicken and rice bowls, 28

L

Lasagna, Turkey, spinach, and mushroom, 174

Leeks

Creamy chicken and corn chowder, 19

Leek and herb-stuffed bacon-wrapped turkey, 203

Slow cooker chicken stew with roasted-pepper rouille, 130

Stovetop cassoulet, 161

Lemons. *See also* Meyer lemons

Basic lemon-herb marinade, 45

Herbed Cornish hens under a brick, 197

Lemon chicken with white beans and stuffed peppers, 133

Lemon-rosemary chicken with radicchio, 128

Moroccan-style chicken with olives, 65

Sautéed chicken thighs with lemon and capers, 26

Lentils

Lentil and chorizo soup with kale, 139

Turkey-lentil curry, 34

Lettuce. *See* Bibb lettuce; Boston lettuce; Kale; Romaine lettuce

Lima beans

Chicken sausages with bean-and-tomato salad, 31

Succotash chicken salad with avocado dressing, 89

Lime

Chicken and corn salad with yogurt-lime dressing, 47

Chicken with couscous-mango salad, 50

Chicken with cucumber, orange, and olive salad, 53

Grilled chicken with shishito peppers, 56

Mojito barbecued chicken, 46

Mustard-glazed chicken salad with mango and lime, 80

M

Mango

Chicken with couscous-mango salad, 50

Indian-spiced chicken with mango raita, 7

Mustard-glazed chicken salad with mango and lime, 80

Vietnamese chicken thighs with mango relish, 61

Maple-glazed Cornish hens with spinach and pear, 198

Marinades, 45

Meatballs, Greek turkey, 177

Meat loaf, Very veggie turkey, 171

Meyer lemons, Roast chicken with, and shallot sauce, 186

Mint

Cajun chicken with minty cucumber-tomato relish, 4

Chicken with grapefruit-mint salsa, 59

Grilled sausage and onion salad with figs, 75

Grilled turkey with watermelon and herb salad, 73

Indian-spiced chicken with mango raita, 7

Mojito barbecued chicken, 46

Mojito barbecued chicken, 46

Montreal chicken rub, 45

Moroccan-style chicken with olives, 65

Moroccan turkey and chickpea soup, 32

Mozzarella cheese

Chicken sausage and mushroom hoagies, 109

Turkey, spinach, and mushroom lasagna, 174

Very veggie turkey meat loaf, 171

Mushrooms

Asian chicken-mushroom soup, 20

Chicken and veggie kebabs with romesco sauce, 62

Chicken pot pie with chive biscuits, 167

Chicken sausage and mushroom hoagies, 109

Chicken vegetable udon soup, 121

Chicken with creamy tarragon-mushroom sauce, 11

Fennel-spiced roast turkey with mushroom gravy, 199

Turkey, spinach, and mushroom lasagna, 174

Turkey mushroom-barley soup with dill, 165

Wild mushroom and sausage risotto, 162

Mustard-glazed chicken salad with mango and lime, 80

N

Napa cabbage

Asian peanut chicken salad, 90

Ginger meatball and vegetable soup, 168

Navel oranges. *See also* Oranges

Chicken with cucumber, orange, and olive salad, 53

Chicken with orange and basil gremolata, 64

Chicken with orange-avocado salsa, 13

O

Oats: Very veggie turkey meat loaf, 171

Olives

Chicken, caramelized onion, and goat cheese pizza, 158

Chicken, spinach, and quinoa salad with olives, 84

Chicken packets with zucchini and tomatoes, 51

Chicken panzanella with peppers and pine nuts, 85

Chicken with cucumber, orange, and olive salad, 53

Chicken with tomato, olive, and feta salad, 60

Moroccan-style chicken with olives, 65

Roast chicken and vegetables provençal, 185

Saffron and tomato chicken with olive couscous, 8

Turkey sausage and roasted potato salad, 99

Onions. *See also* Red onions

Chicken, caramelized, and goat cheese pizza, 158

Open-face cobb salad sandwiches, 102

Open-face Greek turkey burgers, 111

Oranges. *See also* Navel oranges

Chicken salad with farro and squash, 83

Chicken with cucumber, orange, and olive salad, 53

Vietnamese chicken thighs with mango relish, 61

Orecchiette with sausage and broccoli rabe, 39

Oven-barbecued chicken with mop
sauce, 148

P

Panko: Almond chicken cutlets
with tangy cilantro slaw, 14

Parmesan cheese
  Parmesan chicken with fennel-
    arugula salad, 17
  Penne with sausage, white
    beans, and kale, 33

Parsnips: Roast capon with
orange and root veggies, 195

Peanut butter: Asian peanut
chicken salad, 90

Peanuts
  Grilled chicken salad with
    ginger-honey dressing, 18
  Red curry roast chicken with
    coconut sauce, 190
  Thai turkey and broccoli
    stir-fry, 140

Pears, Maple-glazed Cornish hens
with spinach and, 198

Peas. *See also* Snow peas
  Chicken and sausage paella, 157
  Moroccan turkey and chickpea
    soup, 32

Pea shoots: Chicken stir-fry with
black bean sauce, 23

Penne with sausage, white beans,
and kale, 33

Peppercorns
  Brown sugar–brined chicken, 42
  Stir-fry chicken with
    cashews, 22
  Turkey club salad with
    peppercorn salad, 96

Peppers. *See* Bell peppers;
Jalapeño peppers; Roasted
red peppers; Serrano pepper;
Shishito peppers

Peruvian chicken marinade, 45

Pine nuts
  Chicken panzanella with
    peppers and pine nuts, 85
  Grilled sausage and onion salad
    with figs, 75
  Smoky turkey, quinoa, and
    roasted red pepper salad, 95
  Turkey couscous salad with
    dried fruit and pine nuts, 98
  Turkey tortilla wedges with
    arugula and pine nuts, 37

Pizza
  Chicken, caramelized onion, and
    goat cheese pizza, 158
  Chicken, corn, and black bean
    pizza, 165

Plum tomatoes
  Chicken niçoise salad with
    tarragon-olive vinaigrette, 78
  Chicken packets with zucchini
    and tomatoes, 51
  Grilled chicken with tomato-
    anchovy sauce, 54
  Grilled turkey tacos with
    strawberry salsa, 70
  Lentil and chorizo soup with
    kale, 139
  Penne with sausage, white
    beans, and kale, 33
  Roast chicken and vegetables
    provençal, 185
  Southwest turkey and vegetable
    soup, 144
  Tomato-stuffed chicken with
    roasted fennel, 108

Potatoes
  Braised chicken with potatoes
    and artichokes, 131
  Butterflied roast chicken with
    herbed potatoes, 191
  Chicken niçoise salad with
    tarragon-olive vinaigrette, 78

Creamy chicken and corn
  chowder, 19
Roast chicken and vegetables
  provençal, 185
Roast chicken with artichokes
  and potatoes, 189
Rosemary-prosciutto chicken
  with potatoes, 119
Turkey sausage and roasted
  potato salad, 99

Pot pie, chicken, with chive
biscuits, 167

Poultry sausage, 151. *See also*
Chicken sausage; Turkey
sausage

Prosciutto
  Roast chicken prosciutto
    stuffing, 180
  Rosemary-prosciutto chicken
    with potatoes, 119

Q

Quinoa, smoky turkey, and
roasted red pepper salad, 95

R

Radicchio
  Grilled sausage and onion salad
    with figs, 75
  Lemon-rosemary chicken with
    radicchio, 128
  Mustard-glazed chicken salad
    with mango and lime, 80
  Turkey breast with apples,
    fennel, and barley, 201

Radishes
  Asian chicken with carrot-
    cucumber slaw, 55
  Soft turkey tacos with smoky
    tomatillo salsa, 68

Turkey cutlets with couscous-cucumber salad, 71

Red cabbage

Almond chicken cutlets with tangy cilantro slaw, 14

Red curry roast chicken with coconut sauce, 190

Red kidney beans: Turkey, red bean, and chipotle pepper chili, 135

Red onions

Roast capon with orange and root veggies, 195

Roast chicken and vegetables provençal, 185

Saffron and tomato chicken with olive couscous, 8

Slow cooker balsamic-braised chicken with kale, 129

Stir-fry chicken with cashews, 22

Thai ginger-chicken burgers, 103

Relish, Vietnamese chicken thighs with mango, 61

Rice. *See also* Brown rice

Creole Jambalaya, 156

Wild mushroom and sausage risotto, 162

Rice noodles: Thai chicken salad, 92

Ricotta: Turkey, spinach, and mushroom lasagna, 174

Rigatoni with turkey bolognese, 175

Roast capon with bourbon sauce, 192

Roast capon with orange and root veggies, 195

Roast capon with pomegranate glaze, 194

Roast chermoula chicken with butternut squash, 134

Roast chicken and vegetables provençal, 185

Roast chicken prosciutto stuffing, 180

Roast chicken with artichokes and potatoes, 189

Roast chicken with meyer lemons and shallot sauce, 186

Roasted Greek-style chicken and vegetables, 120

Roasted red peppers

Crispy chicken with red pepper sauce, 2

Slow cooker chicken stew with roasted-pepper rouille, 130

Smoky turkey, quinoa, and roasted red pepper salad, 95

Turkey sausage and roasted potato salad, 99

Romaine lettuce

Chicken and corn salad with yogurt-lime dressing, 47

Grilled turkey tacos with strawberry salsa, 70

Mustard-glazed chicken salad with mango and lime, 80

Turkey fattoush salad, 93

Romano cheese

Orecchiette with sausage and broccoli rabe, 39

Rosemary

Lemon-rosemary chicken with radicchio, 128

Rosemary-garlic baked chicken, 116

Rosemary-prosciutto chicken with potatoes, 119

Rotisserie chicken, buying and using, 81

S

Saffron and tomato chicken with olive couscous, 8

Salads

Asian peanut chicken salad, 90

Chicken and corn salad with yogurt-lime dressing, 47

Chicken and grape salad, 86

Chicken milanese with arugula salad, 153

Chicken niçoise salad with tarragon-olive vinaigrette, 78

Chicken salad with farro and squash, 83

Chicken sausages with bean-and-tomato salad, 31

Chicken with couscous-mango salad, 50

Chicken with cucumber, orange, and olive salad, 53

Chicken with tomato-zucchini salad, 48

Grilled chicken salad with ginger-honey dressing, 18

Grilled chicken with cucumber and herb salad, 67

Grilled turkey with watermelon and herb salad, 73

Parmesan chicken with fennel-arugula salad, 17

Succotash chicken salad with avocado dressing, 89

Thai chicken salad, 92

Turkey club salad with peppercorn salad, 96

Turkey fattoush salad, 93

Turkey sausage and roasted potato salad, 99

Salsa

Chicken with grapefruit-mint salsa, 59

Grilled turkey tacos with strawberry salsa, 70

Soft turkey tacos with smoky tomatillo salsa, 68

Sandwiches
Chicken, spinach, and quinoa salad with olives, 84
Chicken bahn mi sandwiches, 101
Chicken panzanella with peppers and pine nuts, 85
Chicken sandwiches with pickled vegetable slaw, 104
Chicken sausage and mushroom hoagies, 109
Chutney chicken sliders, 107
Curried turkey and lentil burgers, 108
Open-face cobb salad sandwiches, 102
Open-face Greek turkey burgers, 111
Thai ginger-chicken burgers, 103
Sautéed chicken thighs with lemon and capers, 26
Serrano pepper: Thai chicken salad, 92
Sheet-pan cheat sheet, 117
Shishito peppers, Grilled chicken with, 56
Shrimp: Creole Jambalaya, 156
Slaw
Almond chicken cutlets with tangy cilantro slaw, 14
Asian chicken with carrot-cucumber slaw, 55
Chicken sandwiches with pickled vegetable slaw, 104
Slow cooker balsamic-braised chicken with kale, 129
Slow cooker chicken stew with roasted-pepper rouille, 130
SmartPoints values, vi, vii
Smoky turkey, quinoa, and roasted red pepper salad, 95
Snow peas
Chicken and eggplant stir-fry with snow peas, 125

Grilled chicken salad with ginger-honey dressing, 18
Soba noodles: Chicken vegetable noodle bowl, 126
Soft turkey tacos with smoky tomatillo salsa, 68
Soups
Asian chicken-mushroom soup, 20
Chicken vegetable udon soup, 121
Creamy chicken and corn chowder, 19
Ginger meatball and vegetable soup, 168
Lentil and chorizo soup with kale, 139
Moroccan turkey and chickpea soup, 32
Southwest turkey and vegetable soup, 144
Turkey mushroom-barley soup with dill, 165
Turkey-tomatillo chili, 143
Southwest turkey and vegetable soup, 144
Spicy farfalle with chicken chorizo and chickpeas, 27
Spinach
Chicken, spinach, and quinoa salad with olives, 84
Chicken stir-fry with black bean sauce, 23
Grilled sausage and onion salad with figs, 75
Maple-glazed Cornish hens with spinach and pear, 198
Moroccan turkey and chickpea soup, 32
Turkey, spinach, and goat cheese enchiladas, 172
Turkey, spinach, and mushroom lasagna, 174

Turkey couscous salad with dried fruit and pine nuts, 98
Turkey cutlets with couscous-cucumber salad, 71
Very veggie turkey meat loaf, 171
Squash. See Butternut squash; Zucchini
Stews, Tuscan sausage and bean, 145
Stir-fries
Chicken and asparagus stir-fry with basil, 25
Chicken and eggplant stir-fry with snow peas, 125
Chicken stir-fry with black bean sauce, 23
Stir-fry chicken with cashews, 22
Thai turkey and broccoli stir-fry, 140
Strawberries, Grilled turkey tacos with, salsa, 70
Succotash chicken salad with avocado dressing, 89
Sweet-and-smoky roast chicken, 182

T

Tacos
Grilled turkey tacos with strawberry salsa, 70
Soft turkey tacos with smoky tomatillo salsa, 68
Tandoori chicken skewers with roasted vegetables, 136
Thai chicken salad, 92
Thai turkey and broccoli stir-fry, 140
Tomatillos
Soft turkey tacos with smoky tomatillo salsa, 68

Turkey, spinach, and goat
cheese enchiladas, 172
Turkey-tomatillo chili, 143
Tomatoes. *See also* Cherry
tomatoes; Grape tomatoes;
Plum tomatoes
Chicken and sausage paella, 157
Chicken and veggie kebabs with
romesco sauce, 62
Chicken ratatouille with
penne, 155
Chicken with tomatoes,
apricots, and chickpeas, 12
Creole Jambalaya, 156
Curried turkey and lentil
burgers, 108
Greek turkey meatballs, 177
Moroccan turkey and
chickpea soup, 32
Open-face cobb salad
sandwiches, 102
Rigatoni with turkey
bolognese, 175
Saffron and tomato chicken
with olive couscous, 8
Slow cooker balsamic-braised
chicken with kale, 129
Slow cooker chicken stew with
roasted-pepper rouille, 130
Stovetop cassoulet, 161
Tomato-stuffed chicken with
roasted fennel, 108
Turkey, red bean, and chipotle
pepper chili, 135
Turkey fattoush salad, 93
Turkey-lentil curry, 34
Tuscan sausage and bean
stew, 145
Tortillas
Grilled turkey tacos with
strawberry salsa, 70
Soft turkey tacos with smoky
tomatillo salsa, 68

Turkey, spinach, and goat
cheese enchiladas, 172
Turkey tortilla wedges with
arugula and pine nuts, 37
Turkey, ground
Turkey, spinach, and mushroom
lasagna, 174
Turkey, whole
Fennel-spiced roast turkey with
mushroom gravy, 199
Turkey bacon
Open-face cobb salad
sandwiches, 102
Succotash chicken salad with
avocado dressing, 89
Turkey club salad with
peppercorn salad, 96
Turkey breast
Leek and herb-stuffed bacon-
wrapped turkey, 203
Moroccan turkey and chickpea
soup, 32
Turkey breast with apples,
fennel, and barley, 201
Turkey couscous salad with
dried fruit and pine nuts, 98
Turkey mushroom-barley soup
with dill, 165
Turkey, ground
Curried turkey and lentil
burgers, 108
Ginger meatball and vegetable
soup, 168
Greek turkey meatballs, 177
Open-face Greek turkey
burgers, 111
Rigatoni with turkey
bolognese, 175
Southwest turkey and vegetable
soup, 144
Turkey, red bean, and chipotle
pepper chili, 135
Turkey, spinach, and goat
cheese enchiladas, 172

Turkey-lentil curry, 34
Turkey tortilla wedges with
arugula and pine nuts, 37
Very veggie turkey meat
loaf, 171
Turkey couscous salad with dried
fruit and pine nuts, 98
Turkey cutlets
Grilled turkey tacos with
strawberry salsa, 70
Grilled turkey with watermelon
and herb salad, 73
Smoky turkey, quinoa, and
roasted red pepper salad, 95
Soft turkey tacos with smoky
tomatillo salsa, 68
Thai turkey and broccoli
stir-fry, 140
Turkey cutlets with couscous-
cucumber salad, 71
Turkey fattoush salad, 93
Turkey sausage
Chicken and sausage paella, 157
Orecchiette with sausage and
broccoli rabe, 39
Penne with sausage, white
beans, and kale, 33
Stovetop cassoulet, 161
Turkey sausage and roasted
potato salad, 99
Tuscan sausage and bean
stew, 145

U

Udon noodles: Chicken vegetable
udon soup, 121

V

Very veggie turkey meat loaf, 171
Vietnamese chicken thighs with
mango relish, 61

W

Watercress
Chicken stir-fry with black bean sauce, 23
Open-face cobb salad sandwiches, 102

Watermelon, Grilled turkey with, and herb salad, 73

White beans: Southwest turkey and vegetable soup, 144

Wild mushroom and sausage risotto, 162

WW Freestyle program, vi

Roast chicken and vegetables provençal, 185

Roasted Greek-style chicken and vegetables, 120

Tandoori chicken skewers with roasted vegetables, 136

Tuscan sausage and bean stew, 145

Very veggie turkey meat loaf, 171

Y

Yogurt. *See also* Greek yogurt
Cajun chicken with minty cucumber-tomato relish, 4
Chicken and corn salad with yogurt-lime dressing, 47
Indian-spiced yogurt marinade, 45
Mustard-glazed chicken salad with mango and lime, 80
Tandoori chicken skewers with roasted vegetables, 136
Turkey-lentil curry, 34

Z

Zucchini
Chicken and veggie kebabs with romesco sauce, 62
Chicken packets with zucchini and tomatoes, 51
Chicken ratatouille with penne, 155
Chicken with tomatoes, apricots, and chickpeas, 12
Chicken with tomato-zucchini salad, 48